THE UNIVERSAL KINSHIP

A Kinship Classic

J. Howard Moore

THE
UNIVERSAL KINSHIP

J. Howard Moore

Edited by
CHARLES MAGEL

CENTAUR PRESS
FONTWELL   SUSSEX

This first paperback edition published 1992
by Centaur Press Ltd, Fontwell, Sussex BN18 0TA

© Centaur Press Ltd, 1992

British Library Cataloguing in Publication Data:
A catalogue record for this book is available
from the British Library

ISBN 0-900001-34-8

Typeset by
Willow-Type, East Dean, Sussex PO18 0JB
Printed and bound by
Antony Rowe Ltd., Chippenham, Wiltshire SN14 6QA

INTRODUCTION

J. Howard Moore: Biographical Fragments

Little is known[1] about the life of J. Howard Moore. My five main sources of information are (1) *Who Was Who in America* (one short paragraph); (2) nineteen letters from Moore to Henry S. Salt (four of which are reproduced in Appendix A); (3) scant autobiographical statements in Moore's publica-

---

[1] In this introduction phrases such as "little is known" or "nothing is known" are to be interpreted as "little is known by me" or "nothing is known by me", etc. There probably exist informative records, documents or letters of which I am unaware.

tions; (4) Clarence Darrow's "A Memorial Address" given at Moore's funeral service (see Appendix B); and (5) *The Humanitarian*, The Journal of the Humanitarian League, London, September 1916 and October 1916 (Henry Salt was the founder and executive secretary of the Humanitarian League).

Moore was born in or near Linden, Missouri[1] on December 4, 1862. Linden is now absorbed into Gladstone in the northern Kansas City metropolitan area. His first name was John; his publications bear the name J. Howard Moore. His mother was Mary Barger Moore, his father William A. Moore. Moore's boyhood recollections suggest life on a northwestern Missouri farm surrounded by wood and stream, teeming with birds and animals, wild and domestic:

> Oh, Rock Creek! Stream that flowed through the Eden of my boyhood! with thy murmurings and thy pools, the pretty fishes, thy cool and solemn groves, the old High Bank, thy golden dreams, thy flowering vales, and thy green hills rolling away! (*The New Ethics*, 158)

[1] *Who Was Who in America* states Linden, Missouri to be his birthplace. *The Humanitarian*, October 1916, reports Moore was born in 1862 in Parke County, Indiana, and was the eldest of a family of six, and that his boyhood was spent on a farm in the Rock Creek Valley, seven miles from Rockport, Indiana. Given that there is a Rock Creek in Linden (now Gladstone), Missouri, and given that Moore himself refers to his boyhood on a northwestern Missouri farm, Linden is probably correct.

> Fido was a shaggy terrier who lived years
> ago in the old home on the farm by the
> beautiful brook. He was one of the very first
> acquaintances the writer of these lines made
> on coming into existence . . . The years have
> been many, and Fido's dust has long been
> scattered by the gusts over the farms of
> northwest Missouri. (*The Universal Kinship*,
> 162-4)[1]

One sibling and a niece or nephew are mentioned in the course of illustrating the individuality of animals — a sister and her baby. (113-4)

We cannot identify Moore's boyhood religion,
but we have ample evidence it was inadequate to
accommodate a universal ethic for all sentient
animals:

> I would like to retain respect for the religion
> of my boyhood, but when I see that religion
> look with indifference, and even levity, upon
> a hemorrhage wide as the continents, . . . not
> only wink at it, but apologise for it, and even
> belittle those few emancipated souls who are
> trying to stop it — I can but feel that such a
> faith has no just claims on the allegiance of
> thinking men. (*The New Ethics*, 46)

As an adult, Moore castigated fishing or hunting
vacations by pastors:

> Hunting and fishing for sport are so plainly

---

[1] Future quotations from *The Universal Kinship* will be
indicated by page numbers only.

> and unexcusably cruel as to excite abhorrence in the mind of any person endowed with the instincts of common sense and humanity. And ministers of the gospel who spend their leisure in such avocations — avocations horrible even to heathens — are either to be pitied for their feeble-mindedness or condemned for their hypocrisy. ("Clerical Sportsmen", *Chicago Vegetarian*, November 1898, 5-6)

From 1880 to 1884 Moore attended Oskaloosa College in Iowa. During the period 1890 to 1893 he taught school (location unknown) and lectured during free intervals in Missouri, Kansas and Iowa, on the topics of temperance and other reforms.

In 1894, aged thirty two, Moore entered the University of Chicago, seeking confirmation of the revolutionary ideas sprouting in his mind:

> Just thirteen years ago the writer of these lines came to the great city in which he now lives from the prairies, with the suspicion which has at last grown into two books, and went around *trying to find out* whether there were any people in the university here or in the world who *lived* the ideas that were just then sprouting doubtfully in his consciousness. And how cold and blind and inhospitable the professional coxcombs here in this great seat of learning were, as they are still today, to these new but blessed ideas. (*The New Ethics*, 144)

Loneliness, the story of Moore's life, accompanied his transition to vegetarianism:

> I became a vegetarian by my reflection. I did not know at the time of the vegetarian movement, and hence, supposed myself alone among republics of carnivora. Nearly every doctrine came to me as a trembling contraband . . . I became a vegetarian for ethical considerations . . . ("Why I Am a Vegetarian", *Chicago Vegetarian*, September 1897, 5)

Moore spent four years at the University of Chicago, receiving the A.B. degree in 1898 (age thirty six), presumably in zoology. The remainder of his professional life was devoted to teaching and lecturing in zoology and ethics in Chicago high schools, principally at Crane Manual Training High School.

In 1899, aged thirty seven, Moore married Jennie Darrow (sister of the famous lawyer Clarence Darrow). There is no mention of children from this marriage.

One receives the impression that Moore was fully understood and appreciated by only one person on this planet — Henry S. Salt, founder and executive secretary of the Humanitarian League in London, and author of the classic *Animals' Rights*[1].

[1] Henry S. Salt, *Animals' Rights* London: Macmillan, 1892. Republished in 1980 by and available from International Society for Animal Rights, Clark's Summit, Pa., and from Centaur Press, Fontwell, Arundel, West Sussex.

In 1899 Moore's first major work, *Better-World Philosphy*, attracted Salt's attention:

> I have a theory that we judge best of the reality of friendships in absence; and if this be true, I cannot have been mistaken as to the warmth of my feelings for Howard Moore, for I never saw him, though we corresponded regularly for years, and I have still a big packet of his letters which show him to have been no less lovable as a man than he was brilliant as a writer . . . It was through a notice which I wrote of a book of his, *Better-World Philosophy* (1899), that I first became associated with him in humanitarian work, and from that time until his death in 1916 he was one of the truest and tenderest of friends . . . (Henry S. Salt, *Company I Have Kept*, London: George Allen and Unwin, 1930, 110)

When *The Universal Kinship* was published in 1906, Salt was unreserved in praise:

> I have long thought that Moore's chief book, *The Universal Kinship*, . . . is the best ever written in the humanitarian cause. (*Company I Have Kept*, 110)

Moore's letters to Salt during the period 1905 to 1915 reveal an unusually warm, affectionate and appreciative friendship. Not only do they esteem the character, intellect and achievements of Salt; they reveal the personality of Moore, and include several autobiographical fragments. Both a century (or two?) ahead of their time, Moore and Salt found deep solace in correspondence with a "fellow crank". Salt's response to a critic might as well have been penned by Moore:

> I felt flattered by the remark of a hostile journalist that I was "a compendium of the Cranks," by which he apparently meant that I advocated not this or that humane reform, but all of them. That is just what I desire to do. (Henry S. Salt, *The Creed of Kinship*)

Excerpts from Moore's letters constitute a veneration of Henry S. Salt:

> I would like to see you, for I am sure you are one of the noblest of this civilization-cursed world. (1905) You realise, don't you Mr. Salt, that you are performing a unique and splendid function in this world? You are producing an enormous effect and one that no one else perhaps has the courage and ability to produce.
>
> There is only one *Henry S. Salt* in the world . . . I often think how much my life would be impoverished if I did not know you . . . The simple fact that you are in the same world with me is to me a great consolation . . . (1906). It is too bad that in the nature of things a Being with your insight and mental vitality, your heroism and power, cannot abide forever in this darkened sphere (3/18/06). I am glad you are on earth. *If it were not for a very few souls like you, this world*

would seem to me an intellectual solitude
(4/20/06). You ought to live among the
earth's highlands somewhere. One whose
soul is so exalted as yours and so touched
with poetry should live close to the sky (10/
2/08). No being in this world more nearly
fulfils my ideal in character and intellect than
you do. It is a continual gratification to me
that my life is being lived in the same
generation with you (7/23/09). I hope I may
meet you sometime. I would desire such an
honour more, did I not have a feeling of my
utter inferiority to you in character and
intellect (11/1/09). Received the half-dozen
copies of "Animals' Rights" which you
kindly sent me . . . The book is a classic on
Humanitarianism, as it deserves to be (1/16/
10). You are the most valuable and successful
humanitarian worker in the world today. I
have always loved you, Mr. Salt, and shall
continue to do so, I am sure, as long as I
breathe (6/13/10). I would gladly give you
ten acres[1] if you'd come over some time and
go down there with me and fall in love with
it (12/4/14). I have been reading your
incomparable "Rights of Animals" again . . .
You seem truly an intellectual brother. I love
you and sincerely hope to be worthy of your
friendship always (11/3/15).

Moore would not have been surprised to learn
that Mohandas Gandhi, on the occasion of a

[1]Moore owned 116½ acres of pristine wood and stream
near Citronelle, Alabama, about thirty three miles from
Mobile.

Vegetarian Society dinner in his honor in 1931, had Salt seated at his right and praised Salt in his address to the large audience.[1]

Moore's letters to Salt are our only source of autobiographical information during the period 1906-1915:

> Oh, nature!— beautiful, peaceful, unirritating, and sublime! Sometimes when I think of the great, slow-sweeping rivers, with prairies and wildernesses, the great, beautiful seas, and the sweet flowers and pretty birds, I feel as if I would like to just go out and put my arms around the whole earth in one giant, magnetic embrace, and melt away and become a part of it . . . *The Universal Kinship* is finished and I hope to offer it to publishers before many weeks or months (1905). As often as I can, I try to snatch a little while from duty and steal away somewhere in some dreamy place and meditate alone . . . We have now in Chicago four vegetarian restaurants that serve together many hundreds of people daily (1906). I am pleased at the favour with which you have greeted my new book "The Universal

---

[1] When Gandhi came to London as a student in 1888 he was a strict vegetarian as the result of a vow made to his mother. Gandhi picked up a copy of Salt's essay "A Plea for Vegetarianism" in a London vegetarian restaurant. Upon reading this essay he became a vegetarian on the basis of principle and choice. Salt's essay also introduced the name Thoreau to Gandhi. Thoreau's essay on civil disobedience later had a profound influence on Gandhi.

Kinship". I have been to a large expense of time and energy in the production of this work. I expect it to be ignored by the ordinary (3/18/06). The little squirrel I sent you by picture is a chipmunk that lived about our cottage in the Adirondacks the past summer . . . "Chippy" came into our cottage and rummaged all about for peanuts and other tidbits for his mid-winter store (11/10/07). Writing is so unnatural and hard for me that I have a good deal of difficulty in getting myself to undergo the hardship. It's a good deal like "sweating blood" for me. And unless I am driven by terrible feelings or convictions, I am inclined to go on and do nothing. I hate writing. It is the greatest hardship of my life (10/2/08). I have been sick for several weeks — two weeks in bed — and am now just getting around again. Then my blessed father has been fading and failing out there on the prairie . . . The coffin is as natural as the cradle (7/23/09). I have just read the November number of your faithful and valiant little journal *Humanity*. I notice your need of money, and I enclose the pitiful little sum of two dollars . . . I am glad you met Mr. Darrow[1] when he was in London, and I am especially glad he met you (11/1/ 09). Over here, we are in the midst of a mild crusade against meat-eating. As usual, the impelling motive is a selfish one — the desire to save a few cents . . . How primitive. How sad. In one sense, how contemptible

---

[1] Clarence Darrow, attorney, brother-in-law of Moore.

(1/27/10). I'm going Saturday morning for a two weeks trip to the Carolina Highlands (4/14/10). I am very busy this fall. My school work has been changed so that it is now largely Ethics. I am expected to teach the 950 boys at the Crane[1] how to act. Besides my regular work I am giving a course of lectures here that required a good deal of preparation (10/29/10). I am down here in this little Alabama town[2] 33 miles from Mobile, getting on my feet again. I haven't been in school since the Christmas holidays. I am much better, and I hope to be back in the Lake Country and at work soon. In the last 16 or 17 years I have written five books. They may never amount to much, but I have given an immense amount of work to their production. I have taught all the time. And my literary work has all been done mornings and evenings, Saturdays and Sundays, and holidays and vacations. And it has been too much for my not naturally strong body (3/25/11). I am going to the blessed acres[3] in the spring . . . Now (in a few days), I shall have 116½ acres there of the loveliest wild woods of pine, poplar, gum, beech, lime oak, magnolia, and holly. I have one holly tree that is over a foot in diameter — and magnolias like sawlogs. In my will I say "My Alabama acres to be kept as they are *forever* — as a sanctuary for the wild things and a

---

[1] Crane Manual Training High School, Chicago.
[2] Citronelle.
[3] In Alabama.

play place for men." People have told me over and over that I will never make anything out of the place. This reminder makes me tired. I wouldn't make anything out of it if I could. I bought it not as an investment, but as an entertainment. It was Mr. E. E. Darrow[1] who first called my place "Alligatoria" . . . There is no building on the place and it is away off from everywhere . . . I can dream there all day and never see any one — except the red birds and squirrels, and great turtles dozing in the sun and the fishes and the great cranes circling above and hear the occasional grunt of an alligator . . . I have about a mile of water front — river and brook (12/4/14).

Do Salt's letters to Moore exist? What an intellectual treat that discovery would be.

On June 17, 1916, aged fifty four, Moore penned his last words:

The long struggle is ended. I must pass away. Good-bye. Oh, men are so cold and hard and half conscious toward their suffering fellows. Nobody understands. O my mother! and O, my little girl! What will become of you? And the poor four footed? May the long years be merciful. Take me to my river. There, where the wild birds sing and the waters go on and on, alone in my groves, forever. O, Tess,[2] forgive me. O, forgive me please. (See Appendix B)

[1] Everett Darrow, brother of Clarence Darrow, brother-in-law of Moore.

[2] Moore's wife. The identity of "my little girl" is unknown.

A British journalist announced that "he died very suddenly." Clarence Darrow avoided euphemism:

> I loved the dead too well to neglect to say what he would have me say, that he put a pistol to his brain and ended his own life. He went out in the morning into Jackson Park,[1] on the wooded island, the place he loved, where for years he had listened to his friends, the song birds, lay down upon the grass, put a pistol to his head and sent a bullet through his brain ... The dead left his request that his ashes should be taken to his wild wood home in Alabama and laid beside the river in the forest where he could sleep in peace forever. (See Appendix B for Darrow's complete memorial address)

[1] Jackson Park, Chicago. Moore's principal residence in Chicago was near Jackson Park at 6260 Jackson Park Avenue. In a letter of January 6, 1906, from Everett Darrow to Moore, Darrow refers to a severe operation which Moore had undergone — so serious that Darrow states he would never have had the nerve to risk it. According to *The Chicago Sunday Tribune*, June 18, 1916:
"He had been in ill health for many years and began to decline definitely after an operation five years ago."

J. Howard Moore's *The Universal Kinship* and Peter Singer's *Animal Liberation*[1]

The prospective reader of *The Universal Kinship* is likely to be familiar with Peter Singer's influential *Animal Liberation*. To facilitate an understanding of Moore's views it may be helpful to call attention to several similarities and dissimilarities in these two important works.

Given that Moore is a zoologist writing in 1905, and Singer a philosopher writing in 1975, we expect sharp differences in content and structure. Nearly 25% of *Animal Liberation* is a detailed description of the manner and extent to which animals are harmed in experiments and safety tests. In Moore's book there are few incidental references to vivisection, the term in vogue in his day.[2] At that time vivisection consisted often of demonstrations in physiological classes and in medical schools. Psychological experiments and safety tests on animals were not extensive. Another 25% of Singer's book is devoted to a detailed description of the manner and extent to which

---

[1] *Animal Liberation: A New Ethics for Our Treatment of Animals,* New York: Avon Books, 1977 (first published in 1975 by New York Review).

[2] Moore's principal discussion of vivisection appears in "Discovering Darwin", an address published in *Proceedings of the International Anti-Vivisection and Animal Protection Congress,* Washington D.C., December 8-11, 1913. "There is not a vivisector on the face of the earth who would carry on his work more than a minute or two if he had himself to undergo the experiences which he inflicts on his victims." (157).

animals are harmed by intensive, confining fac-
tory-farming methods of raising animals for food.
Factory farming did not exist in 1906, and Moore
restricts himself, in *The Universal Kinship*, to
several incidental references to the use of animals
for food. About 10% of *Animal Liberation* is on
the topic of becoming a vegetarian. Moore's treatment of vegetarianism is in a series of articles
published in 1897.[1] Singer reminds his reader that
"nowhere in this book... do I appeal to the reader's
emotions where they cannot be supported by reason" (xi). In fact, Singer tells us that other than his
interest in the prevention of suffering and misery,
and in opposing wrongful exploitation, he is not
especially "interested in" animals; he has no pets,
and is not inordinately fond of cats, dogs or horses
(x). Moore, also, uses scientific fact and reason to
support his views. But he is intensely interested in
animals, and there are occasions when his emotions break through.[2]

The first section of *The Universal Kinship* is
titled "The Physical Kinship". The other animals
are our *physical* cousins. As well explained by
Charles Darwin in *The Origin of Species* (1859),
and in *The Descent of Man* (1871), human animals
and the other animals all evolved from other life
forms through the selective processes of variation

---

[1] "Why I Am a Vegetarian", *Chicago Vegetarian*, September
1897, 5-9; October 1897, 5-7; November 1897, 8-12;
December 1897, 7-11, 16, 18.
[2] Moore is rather successful in restraining his emotions in
The Universal Kinship. In *The New Ethics*, published a
year later, his emotions are given free rein.

and heredity in interaction with the environment. There is no qualitative gulf between the physical characteristics of human and other animals; rather, there is a continuity. Human animals did not come into existence by a special event of creation:

> But man *is* an *animal* . . . an animal in the most literal and materialistic meaning of the word. Man has not a spark of so-called "divinity" about him . . . In origin, disposition and form he is no more "divine" than the dog who laps his sores, the terrapin who waddles over the earth in a carapace, or the unfastidious worm who dines on the dust of his feet. He . . . has been brought into existence by the same evolutional processes as the horse, the toad . . ., the firefly . . ., and the bivalve that reluctantly feeds him (4-5). There are, in fact, no gulfs anywhere, only gradations (26). Man is simply one portion of the immense enterprise . . . He is not a celestial star-babe dropped down among mundane matters for a time and endowed with wing possibilities and the anatomy of a deity (100-1).

Whereas Moore devotes many pages to the nature of, and evidences for, evolution, Singer takes for granted the fact of evolution and its implications:

> Intellectually, the Darwinian revolution was genuinely revolutionary. Human beings now knew that they were not the special creation of God, made in the divine image and set

apart from the animals; on the contrary,
human beings came to realise that they were
animals themselves . . . The scientific
evidence for a common origin of the human,
and other species was . . . overwhelming
(214-5).

The Darwinian revolution is far from permeating the public mind. In 1991 a Gallup Poll[1] was taken in the United States with the following results: 47% of Americans thought humans were created by God in the last 10,000 years. 25% of American college graduates believed humans were created by God in the last 10,000 years.

The second section of *The Universal Kinship* is entitled "The Psychical Kinship". The other animals are our *mental* cousins. As so well described by Darwin in his "Comparison of the Mental Powers of Man and the Lower Animals" (1871) and *The Expression of the Emotions in Man and Animals* (1872), the mental characteristics of human animals and the other animals all evolved from other life forms through the selective processes of variation and heredity in interaction with the environment. There is no *qualitative* gulf between the mental characteristics of human and other animals; rather, there is a continuity, paralleling the continuity of physical characteristics. Mental capacities vary in *degree*. Human mental capacities did not come into existence by a special event of creation:

[1] Reported in the *Los Angeles Times*, May 2, 1992.

The jelly-fish and the philosopher are not mental aliens. They are linked to each other by a continuous gradation of intermediate intelligences (112). We are almost as ignorant of the mental life and personality of these door-yard neighbours and friends of ours as we would be if they were the inhabitants of another continent (113). Each [human] individual mind ascends through a series of mental faculties which epitomises in a remarkable manner the psychogenesis of the animal kingdom (137). Just the ordinary observation of them [animals] in their daily lives about us . . . is sufficient to convince any person of discernment that they are beings with joys and sorrows, desires and capabilities, similar to our own . . . They . . . seek pleasure and try to avoid pain . . . (146). The non-human races of the earth are *not* the metallic and soulless lot of fixtures they are vulgarly supposed to be; . . . they are just as real living beings, with just as precious nerves and just as genuine feelings, rights, heartaches, capabilities, and waywardness, as we ourselves (195). The chief powers of the mind of man are *sensation, memory, emotion, imagination, volition, instinct* and *reason*. All of these faculties are found in non-human beings, some of them developed to a much higher degree than they are in man, and some of them to a much lower (196). Man is not a fallen god, but a promoted reptile. The beings around him are not conveniences, but cousins[1] (107). All terrestrial races (unless the very lowest) have the power of experiencing two kinds of conscious states — the desirable (pleasurable) and the undesirable (painful) . . . The pleasurable experiences are the experiences all beings are seeking, and the painful ones they are all seeking to avoid (292). In plants . . . there is an almost total absence of the evidence relied on to prove consciousness in animals . . . Plants are wholly devoid of a nervous system . . . The fact that plants display intelligence by adapting their acts to ends is no evidence whatever that they are conscious. If intelligence be defined as the adjustment of acts to ends, then a large part of terrestrial intelligence . . . is unconscious and mechanical (*The New Ethics*, 170, 172). Every sentient creature is struggling — struggling for adaptation — struggling to keep itself in joint with the environment ("Why I Am a Vegetarian", *Chicago Vegetarian*, September 1897, 5). Just where consciousness sets in, either in the individual or in the zoological process as a whole, it is at this time impossible to say . . . We infer the consciousness of a dog or an insect in the same way we infer the consciousness of a savage or a member of our own family . . .

---

[1] In 1923 Henry Salt dedicated his *The Story of My Cousins* "To the memory of my friend, Howard Moore, author of 'The Universal Kinship'". This book contains brief biographies of a dog, cats, and a bird, all cousin friends of Salt's.

> Now, animals — all the vertebrates, anyway,
> and many of the invertebrates — are so
> similar to men in their organization and in
> their general nervous makeup and modes of
> life and expression that we are compelled to
> suppose that they possess, in an ever-
> diminishing intensity as we go downward in
> the zoological scale, a conscious existence
> similar to our own . . . It may well be doubted
> whether the simplest animals, like the coral,
> and the one-celled forms, have anything
> corresponding to what we know or think of
> as sentiency (*The New Ethics*, 170-3).

Singer's common-sense view of the mental powers of animals is essentially similar to Darwin's.
Many non-human animals are sentient, that is, they
are conscious and have the capacity to suffer and/
or experience enjoyment or happiness:[1]

> . . . There are no good reasons, scientific or
> philosophical, for denying that animals feel
> pain. If we do not doubt that other humans
> feel pain we should not doubt that other
> animals do so too (15) . . . I propose to use
> "person" . . . in the sense of a rational and
> self-conscious being . . . Some non-human
> animals are persons, as we have defined the
> term . . . Chimpanzees may be the clearest
> case of non-human persons . . . It is quite
> possible that these large-brained mammals
> [whales and dolphins] will turn out to be
> rational and self-conscious . . . Closer to

---

[1] *Animal Liberation*, 8-9.

home, many of those who live with dogs and cats are convinced that these animals are self-conscious and rational . . . And if dogs and cats qualify as persons, the mammals we use for food cannot be far behind . . . Pigs are highly intelligent animals . . . Are we turning persons into bacon? . . . It is notoriously difficult to establish when another being is self-conscious. But if . . . there is real doubt about whether a being we are thinking of killing is a person, we should give that being the benefit of the doubt. (*Practical Ethics*, Cambridge: Cambridge University Press, 1979, pp. 76, 97-9) . . . I gave three distinct grounds for believing that non-human animals can feel pain: behaviour, the nature of their nervous systems, and the evolutionary usefulness of pain. None of these gives us any reason to believe that plants feel pain (248). Where exactly do we draw the line? . . . The problem of drawing the line is the problem of deciding when we are justified in assuming that a being is incapable of suffering . . . With birds and mammals the evidence is overwhelming [that they can suffer] . . . Fish and reptiles show most of the pain behaviour that mammals do . . . Crustaceans — crabs, shrimps, prawns, lobsters — have nervous systems . . . do act as if they feel pain . . . There may be room for doubt, but it does seem that crust-aceans deserve the benefit of the doubt . . . Most mollusks [oysters, clams, mussels, scallops, etc.] are such rudimentary beings that it is difficult to imagine them feeling pain, or having mental states . . . Somewhere between a shrimp and an oyster seems as good a place to draw the line as any, and better than most (174-9).

Neither Moore nor Singer is dogmatic in his attempt to draw the line between sentient and non-sentient animals. Moore is a bit more conservative, drawing a grey line between the jelly-fish and the sponge. But they are in the same general area.

The final section of *The Universal Kinship* bears the title "The Ethical Kinship". Given that the other animals are our physical and mental cousins, the same ethical principles are to be universally applied to all sentient animals — human and non-human. The anthropocentric ethic — the view that only human interests count and that the other animals are mere instruments to serve human interests — is as immoral as viewing women or blacks as instruments to serve men or whites. Sentiency is the criterion for determining whether a being should be given ethical consideration. Actions are right to the extent they maximize pleasure and minimize pain for all sentient beings, and wrong to the extent they do not. The impartial feature of this universal ethic is profoundly captured in the Golden Rule:

Man is simply *one* of a *series* of sentients, differing in degree, but not in kind, from the beings below, above and around him. *The Great Law — Act toward others as you would act toward a part of your own self —* is a law not applicable to Aryans only, but to all men, and not to men only, but to *all*

beings . . . But in the application of this rule
human beings restrict it hypocritically to the
members of their own species . . . Our own
happiness, and that of our species, are
assumed to be so pre-eminent that we sacrifice
the most sacred interests of others . . . (*The
New Ethics*, 15, 40-1). *The same general
moral code applies to every being that
feels* ("Discovering Darwin," 156). Not to
the black man and the white woman alone,
but to the sorrel horse and the grey squirrel
as well. Yes, do as you would be done — not
to creatures of your own anatomy or your
own guild only, but to all creatures ("Why I
Am a Vegetarian," *Chicago Vegetarian*,
December 1897, 10). *Moral obligation is
as extensive as the power to feel* (*The New
Ethics*, 17). Right and wrong are, and they
are because there are creatures susceptible of
happiness and misery. Erase sentiency from
the universe and you erase the possibility of
ethics. I have, therefore, ethical relations to
the Eskimo and the oyster, but not to the
cabbage and the clod, because the ones are
sensible and the others are not ("Why I Am
a Vegetarian," *Chicago Vegetarian*,
September 1897, 8). *The only rational
method of judging conduct, and the only
method that should ever be employed by
beings pretending to be logical or civilized,
is to balance the effects which the act on
trial has on the different interests, and then
render a verdict from the standpoint of this
balance, which is the standpoint of the
universe* (*The New Ethics*, 52-3). The
pleasurable experiences are the experiences

all beings are seeking, and the painful ones
are the ones they are all seeking to avoid.
Those acts which help or tend to help beings
to those experiences for which they are
striving are, therefore, right and proper . . .
and their authors called *good*. While those
acts which compel beings to undergo that
which they are striving to avoid are improper
and wrong . . . and their authors are *bad*.
Kindness, courtesy, justice, mercy,
generosity, sympathy, love, and the like, are
good, and selfishness, cruelty, deceit, pillage,
injustice, and murder, are bad, because they
are respectively the promoters and destroyers
of well-being and happiness in the world
(292-3).

Several early readers of *Animal Liberation*, including a couple of philosophers who should have
read more carefully, jumped to the conclusion that
Singer was espousing a rights theory for animals,
merely because the word "rights" occasionally
appears. A close reading reveals that the term
"rights" occurs mainly in the context of *ad hominem*
arguments against those who do hold a rights
theory. Singer does not hold a rights theory —
either for human animals or non-human animals.[1]
In *The Universal Kinship* the term "rights" occurs
very rarely, and there is no suggestion that Moore
is interested in a rights theory for animals.

Although Singer does not explictly emphasize

---

[1] "Animal Liberation or Animal Rights?" *Monist* 70
(1987), p.4.

it, the ethical theory structuring *Animal Liberation* is utilitarian, similar to Moore's utilitarianism:

> The capacity for suffering and enjoyment is *a prerequisite for having interests at all*, a condition that must be satisfied before we can speak of interests in a meaningful way. It would be nonsense to say that it was not in the interests of a stone to be kicked along the road by a school boy. A stone does not have interests because it cannot suffer . . . A mouse, on the other hand, does have an interest in not being kicked along the road, because it will suffer if it is . . . If a being suffers there can be no moral justification for refusing to take that suffering into consideration. No matter what the nature of the being, the principle of equality requires that its suffering be counted equally with the like suffering of any other being . . . So the limit of sentience . . . is the only defensible boundary of concern for the interests of others . . . The racist violates the principle of equality by giving greater weight to the interests of his own race . . . The sexist violates the principle of equality by favouring the interests of his own sex. Similarly, the speciesist allows the interests of his own species to override the greater interests of members of other species . . . Most human beings are speciesists (8-9). Pain and suffering are bad, and should be prevented or minimized, irrespective of the race, sex, or species of the being that suffers (18) . . . The conclusions that are argued for in this book flow from the principle of minimizing

suffering alone. (22).

Singer's utilitarianism leads to vegetarianism:

> I am a utilitarian. I am also a vegetarian. I am
> a vegetarian because I am a utilitarian. I
> believe that applying the principle of utility
> to our present situation . . . leads to the
> conclusion that we ought to be vegetarian
> ("Utilitarianism and Vegetarianism,"
> *Philosophy and Public Affairs* 1980, 9:325-
> 37).

According to Singer, it is theoretically conceivable that the equality principle and utilitarianism could justify some harmful research on animals so that humans benefit, also some harmful research on humans so that animals benefit. "In practice, though, I am convinced that the best way to advance the interests of animals and humans would be to stop all harmful research on animals, and use the money thereby saved in other more productive ways" ("Letter on Animal Liberation," *Animals' Agenda*, 7, December 1987:3).

The theoretical foundations of *The Universal Kinship* and *Animal Liberation* are essentially identical. Practical conclusions on how we should treat animals are similar.

San Diego
California, 1992   C.M.

ACKNOWLEDGEMENTS

I thank Jon Wynne-Tyson for the privilege of introducing J. Howard Moore to the present generation; Bernard Unti for the opportunity to spend four days in his splendid historical library on animals and for providing many materials; George Hendrick for channeling to me materials on Moore and Salt and for editorial advice; Randall Tietjen for discovering the Moore letters, the Moore photograph, the Clarence Darrow memorial address, and for making these invaluable materials available to me; and Blanche Chase and Mary Simonson, granddaughters of Clarence Darrow, for permission to reproduce the Moore letters and the Moore photograph.

THE KINSHIP LIBRARY

"The cause of each and all of the evils that afflict the world is the same — the general lack of humanity, the lack of the knowledge that all sentient life is akin, and that he who injures a fellow being is in fact doing injury to himself."

Henry Salt: *Seventy Years Among Savages*

THE KINSHIP LIBRARY, to meet the growing demand from those concerned by the rising tide of human and animal suffering, offers work tracing the connection between our often lamentable behaviour toward each other, and our thoughtless and cruel exploitation of non-human species.

This aspect of humane education, given scant attention until recently, is becoming of major concern. The implications of Albert Schweitzer's perception that "until he extends the circle of his compassion to all living things, man will not himself find peace" are vital to any real growth in education. They explore the deepest level of the environmental conscience and have particular significance for students, teachers, and those most responsibly engaged in furthering the welfare and rights of animals.

The Kinship Library will present new books on the philosophy, politics and implications of those rights, and reissues of long unobtainable works of special merit, edited or introduced by modern scholars. The older reissues will be published as Kinship Classics.

Editorial advisors to The Kinship Library: Maureen Duffy; Audrey Eyton; George Hendrick; Charles Magel; Jan Morris; Tom Regan; Richard D. Ryder; Peter Singer; John Stockwell.

PUBLISHER'S NOTE

Other Kinship Library titles published or pending include:

Moral Inquiries on the Situation of Man and of Brutes by Lewis Gompertz, edited by Peter Singer.

The Duty of Mercy by Humphry Primatt, edited and introduced by Richard D. Ryder.

All Heaven in a Rage by E.S. Turner.

On Abstinence from Animal Food by Joseph Ritson, introduced by Keith Tester.

Also an edited reissue of Edward Maitland's *Life of Anna Kingsford*; John Oswald's *The Cry of Nature*; E.W.B. Nicholson's *The Rights of an Animal*; William Youatt's *The Obligation and Extent of Humanity to Brutes*; Thomas Young's *Essay on Humanity to Animals*; Henry Salt's *Seventy Years Among Savages*; E.D. Buckner's *The Immortality of Animals*; J. Howard Moore's *The New Ethics*; selections from the works of J. Todd Ferrier, Thomas Tryon, Lord (Thomas) Erskine, Howard Williams, Francis Newman, J.A. Gleizes, J.F. Newton, Pierre Lotti, J.L. Joynes, Lady Florence Dixie, William Lambe, Jeremy Bentham, Ernest Bell and others. New books by modern philosophers and writers will be announced.

COVER: Naming the animals: from a fourth-century ivory.

A Sacred Kinship I would not forgo
Binds me to all that breathes.

HJALMAR HJORTH BOYESEN, 1848-1895

PREFACE

THE Universal Kinship means the kinship of all
the inhabitants of the planet Earth. Whether
they came into existence among the waters or
among desert sands, in a hole in the earth, in the
hollow of a tree, or in a palace ; whether they
build nests or empires ; whether they swim, fly,
crawl, or ambulate ; and whether they realise it
or not, they are all related, physically, mentally,
morally—this is the thesis of this book. But
since man is the most gifted and influential of
animals, and since his relationship with other
animals is more important and more reluctantly
recognised than any other, the chief purpose of
these pages is to prove and interpret the kinship
of the human species with the other species of
animals.

The thesis of this book comes pretty squarely
in conflict with widely-practised and highly-prized
sins. It will therefore be generally criticised
where it is not passed by in silence. Men as a
rule do not care to improve. Although they have

but one life to live, they are satisfied to live the thing out as they have started on it.

Enthusiasm, which in an enlightened or ideal race would be devoted to self-improvement, is used by men in weaving excuses for their own inertia or in singing of the infirmities of others.

But there is a Future. And the creeds and ideals men bow down to to-day will in time to come pass away, and new creeds and ideals will claim their allegiance. Shrines change as the generations come and go, and out of the decomposition of the old comes the new. The time will come when the sentiments of these pages will not be hailed by two or three, and ridiculed or ignored by the rest ; *they will represent Public Opinion and Law.*

M.

CHICAGO, 1905.

CONTENTS

THE PHYSICAL KINSHIP

THE PSYCHICAL KINSHIP

CONTENTS

THE ETHICAL KINSHIP

APPENDICES

THE UNIVERSAL KINSHIP

THE PHYSICAL KINSHIP

'LIKE the Roman emperors, who, intoxicated by their power, at length regarded themselves as demigods, so the ruler of the earth believes that the animals subjected to his will have nothing in common with his own nature. Man is not content to be the king of animals. He insists on having it that an impassable gulf separates him from his subjects. The affinity of the ape disturbs and humbles him. And, turning his back upon the earth, he flies, with his threatened majesty, into the cloudy sphere of a special "human kingdom." But Anatomy, like those slaves who followed the conqueror's car crying, "Thou art a man," disturbs him in his self-admiration, and reminds him of those plain and tangible realities which unite him with the animal world.'— BROCA.

THE UNIVERSAL KINSHIP

THE PHYSICAL KINSHIP

I. Man an Animal.

IT was in the zoology class at college. We had made all the long journey from amœba to coral, from coral to worm, from worm to mollusk, from mollusk to fish, from fish to reptile, and from reptile to mammal—and there, in the closing pages of faithful old Packard, we found it. 'A mammal of the order of primates,' the book said, with that unconcern characteristic of the deliverances of science. I was almost saddened. It was the first intimation I had ever received of that trite but neglected truth that *man is an animal*.

But the intimation was so weak, and I was at that time so unconscious, that it was not till years later that I began, through reflection, actually to realise the truth here first caught sight of. During these years I knew that man was not a mineral nor a plant—that, indeed, he belonged to the

3

animal kingdom. But, like most men still, I continued to think of him as being altogether different from other animals. I thought of man *and the animals, not* of man and the *other* animals. Man was somehow *sui generis.* He had had, I believed, a unique and miraculous origin ; for I had not yet learned of organic evolution. The pre-Darwinian belief that I had come down from the skies, and that non-human creatures of all kinds had been brought into existence as adjuncts of the distinguished species to which I belonged, occupied prominent place in my thinking. Non-human races, so I had been taught, had *in themselves* no reason for existence. They were accessories. A chasm, too wide for any bridge ever to span, yawned between the human and all other species. Man was celestial, a blue-blood barely escaping divinity. All other beings were little higher than clods. So faithfully and mechanically did I reflect the bias in which I had grown up.

But man *is* an *animal.* It was away out there on the prairies, among the green corn rows, one beautiful June morning—a long time ago it seems to me now—that this revelation really came to me. And I repeat it here, as it has grown to seem to me, for the sake of a world which is so wise in many things, but so darkened and wayward regarding this one thing. However averse to accepting it we may be on account of favourite traditions, man is an animal in the most literal and materialistic meaning of the word. Man has not a spark of so-called ' divinity ' about him. In important respects he is the most highly evolved of animals; but in origin, disposition, and form he is no more 'divine' than the dog who laps his sores, the terrapin who waddles over the earth in a carapace, or the unfastidious worm who dines on the dust of his feet. Man is not the pedestalled individual pictured by his imagination—a being glittering with prerogatives, and towering apart from and above all other beings. He is a pain-shunning, pleasure-seeking, death-dreading organism, differing in particulars, but not in kind, from the pain-shunning, pleasure-seeking, death-dreading organisms below and around him. Man is neither a rock, a vegetable, nor a deity. He belongs to the same class of existences, and has been brought into existence by the same evolutional processes, as the horse, the toad that hops in his garden, the firefly that lights its twilight torch, and the bivalve that reluctantly feeds him.

Man's body is composed fundamentally of the same materials as the bodies of all other animals. The bodies of all animals are composed of clay. They are formed of the same elements as those that murmur in the waters, gallop in the winds, and constitute the substance of the insensate rocks and soils. More than two-thirds of the weight of the human body is made up of oxygen alone, a gas which forms one-fifth of the weight of the air, more than eight-ninths of that of the sea, and forty-seven per cent. of the superficial solids of the earth.

Man's body is composed of cells. So are the

bodies of all other animals. And the cells in the body of a human being are not essentially different in composition or structure from the cells in the body of the sponge. All cells are composed primarily of protoplasm, a compound of carbon, hydrogen, nitrogen, and oxygen. Like all other animals, man is incapable of producing a particle of the essential substance of which his body is made. No animal can produce protoplasm. This is a power of the plant, and the plant only. All that any animal can do is to burn the compounds formed in the sun-lit laboratories of the vegetable world. The human skeleton, like the skeletons of nearly all other animals, is composed chiefly of ime—lime being, in the sea, where life spent so many of its earlier centuries, the most available material for parts whose purpose it is to furnish shape and durability to the organism. Man grows from an egg. So do all creatures of clay. Every animal commences at the same place—in a single, lowly, almost homogeneous cell. A dog, a frog, a philosopher, and a worm cannot for a long time after their embryonic commencement be distinguished from each other. Like the oyster, the ox, the insect, and the fish, like all that live, move, and breathe, man is mortal. He increases in size and complexity through an allotted period of time; then, like all his kindred, wilts back into the indistinguishable flux from which he came. Man inhales oxygen and exhales carbon dioxide. So does every animal that breathes, whether it breathe by lungs, gills, skin, or ectosarc, and whether it breathe the sunless ooze of the sea floor or the ethereal blue of the sky. Animals inhale oxygen because they eat carbon and hydrogen. The energy of all animals is produced mainly by the union of oxygen with the elements of carbon and hydrogen in the tissues of animal bodies, the plentiful and ardent oxygen being the most available supporter of the combustion of these two elements.

Man is, then, an animal, more highly evolved than the most of his fellow-beings, but positively of the same clay, and of the same fundamental make-up, with the same eagerness to exceed and the same destiny, as his less pompous kindred who float and frolic and pass away in the seas and atmospheres, and creep over the land-patches of a common clod.

II. Man a Vertebrate.

Man is a *vertebrate* animal.* He has (anatomically at least) a backbone. He belongs to that substantial class of organisms possessing an articulating internal skeleton—the family of the fishes, amphibians, reptiles, birds, and mammals. Most animals have some sort of skeleton, some sort of calcareous contrivance, whose business it is to give form and protection to the softer parts of the organism. Some animals, as the star-fishes, have plates of lime scattered throughout the surface parts of the body; others, as the corals

---

* See 'Classes of Animals,' p. 330.

and sponges, secrete plant-like frames, upon and among the branches of which the organisms reside ; and still others, as the clams, crustaceans, and insects, have skeletons consisting of a shell or sheath on the outside of, and more or less surrounding, the softer substances of the body. The limbs of insects are tiny tubes on the inside of which are the miniature muscles with which they perform their marvels of locomotion. The skeleton of vertebrates, consisting of levers, beams, columns, and arches, all skilfully joined together and sunk deep within the muscular tissue, forms a conspicuous contrast to the rudimentary frames of other animals. The vertebrate skeleton consists of a hollow axis, divided into segments and extending along the dorsal region of the body, from the ventral side of which articulate, by means of awkwardly-constructed girdles, an anterior and a posterior pair of limbs. This dorsal axis ends in front in a peculiar bulbous arrangement called the head, which contains, among other valuables, the brain and buccal cavern. The thoracic segments of the backbone send off pairs of flat bones, which, arching ventrally, form the chest for the protection of the heart and other vitals. The limbs (except in fishes) consist each of a single long bone, succeeded by two long bones, followed by two transverse rows of short, irregular wrist or ankle bones, ending normally in five branching series of bones called digits. This is essentially the skeleton of all fishes, amphibians, reptiles, birds, and mammals. In short, it is the universal vertebrate

type of frame. There are minor modifications to
suit the various kinds of environment, adaptations
to the necessities of aquatic, terrestrial, and aerial
locomotion and life, some parts being specialised,
others atrophied, and still others omitted, but
there is never anywhere, from fishes to philosophers, any fundamental departure from the established vertebrate type of skeleton.* The pectoral
fins of fishes correspond to the fore-limbs of frogs
and reptiles, the wings of birds, and the arms of
men. The pelvic fins of fishes are homologous
with the hind-limbs of frogs, reptiles, and quadrupeds, and the legs of birds, apes, and men.
The foot of the dog and crocodile, the hand of the
orang, and the flipper of the dolphin and seal, all
have the same general structure as the hand of
man ; and the wings of the bat and bird, the fore-
limbs of the lizard and elephant, and the comical
shovels of the mole and ornithorhynchus, notwithstanding the great differences in their external
appearance and use, contain essentially the same
bones and the same arrangement of the bones as
do the arms of men and women. The human
body has two primary cavities in it. So have the
bodies of all vertebrates: a neural cavity containing the brain and spinal cord, and a visceral
cavity containing the heart, liver, lungs, and
alimentary canal. Invertebrates have only one

* Snakes are limbless, and hind-limbs are lacking in
whales and other degenerates ; but rudimentary limbs are
found in the embryonic stages of these animals. Frogs, it
may be said also, have no ribs.

body cavity—the one corresponding to the visceral cavity of vertebrates—and the main nerve trunk, instead of extending along the back, as among vertebrates, is in invertebrates located ventrally. Vertebrates are the only animals on the earth that have a highly developed circulatory system, a system entirely shut off from the other systems, and containing a heart, arteries, veins, and capillaries. In all invertebrates the digestive and circulatory systems remain to a greater or less extent connected, the blood and food mingling more or less in the general cavity of the body. Worms and insects have pulsating tubes instead of heart and arteries. Crustaceans have hearts with one chamber, and mollusks have two or three chambered hearts, but the blood, instead of returning to the heart after its journey through the arteries, passes into the body cavity. In man and other vertebrates the circulating current is confined strictly to the bloodvessels, no particle of it ever escaping into the general body cavity. The heart of vertebrates is distinguished from that of invertebrates by being located ventrally. The heart of invertebrates is in the back. The blood of vertebrates differs from that of invertebrates in containing both red and white corpuscles. Invertebrates have white corpuscles only. Worms have yellow, red, or bright green blood. The blood of crustaceans is bluish, that of mollusks is white, and that of insects dusky or brown. The blood of all vertebrates, excepting amphioxus, is red. All backboned beings, whether they dwell in seas or cities, and whether they build nests or empires, have two eyes, two ears, nose and mouth, all located in the head, and always occupying the same relative position to each other. Invertebrates may have their brains in their abdomen, as do the mites; hear with their legs or antennæ, as many insects do; see with their tunics, like the scallops; and breathe with their skin, as do the worms. The crayfish hears with its 'feelers,' the cricket and katydid with their fore-legs, the grasshopper with its abdomen, the clam with its 'foot,' and mysis and other low crustaceans have their auditory organs on their tails.

Man is, then, like the fishes, frogs, reptiles, birds, and quadrupeds, a vertebrate animal. Excepting in his infancy, when he is a quadruped going on all fours, he uses his posterior limbs only for locomotion, and his anterior for prehension and the like. His spinal axis is erect instead of horizontal, and his tail is atrophied. But he possesses all of the unmistakable qualities of the vertebrate type of structure—a two-chambered body cavity, a highly developed and dorsally located nerve trunk, vertebrate vitals, a closed circulatory system, a ventral heart, red blood, a head containing sense organs and brain, and a well-ordered internal skeleton, consisting of a vertebral column with skull and ribs and two pairs of limbs, the limbs consisting each of one long bone, two long bones, two transverse rows of irregular bones, and five branches at the end.

III. Man a Mammal.

Man is a *mammal*. He belongs to the most brilliant and influential of the five classes of verte-brates—the class to which belong so many of his associates and victims, the class to which belong the horse, the dog, the deer, the ox, the sheep, the swine, the squirrel, the camel, the unattenuated elephant, and the timid-hearted hare. To this class belong also the lion, the tiger, the kangaroo, the beaver, the bear, the bat, the monkey, the mole, the wolf, the ornithorhynchus, and the whale—in short, *all animals that have hair*. Fishes and reptiles have scales; birds have feathers; all mammals are covered to a greater or less extent with hair. The aquatic habits of whales render hair of no use to them. Hence, while the unborn of these animals still cling to the structural tradi-tions of their ancestors and are covered with hair, the adults are almost hairless. The sartorial habits of human beings and the selective influ-ences of the sexes have had a similar effect on the hairy covering of the human body. Hair exists all over the human body surface, excepting on the soles of the hands and feet, but in a greatly dwarfed condition. It is only on the scalp and on the faces of males, where it is scientifically assisted for purposes of display, that it grows luxuriantly. It is by no means certain that even the hair on the masculine scalp will last forever. For if the hermetical derby and other deadly devices worn by men continue their devastations

as they have in the past, we may expect to have,
in the course of generations, men with foreheads
reaching regularly to the occiput.   Most animals
lay eggs.   Man does not.   Like the dog, the
horse, the squirrel, and the bat, man is viviparous,
the eggs hatching within the parental body.
Human young are born helpless, and are sustained during the period of their infancy by the
secretions of the milk glands.   So are all the sons
and daughters of mammals.   Whether they come
into the world among the waters or among the
desert sands, in the hollow of a tree, in a hole in
the earth, or in a palace, the children of mammals
are frail and pitiful, and they survive to grow and
multiply only because they are the object of the
loving and incessant sacrifices of a mother.

Mammals are distinguished from all other
animals by the possession of two kinds of skin
glands—the sweat glands and the oil glands—and
by the development of certain of these glands in
the female into organs for the nourishing of the
young.   Among reptiles and birds the lower jaw
is suspended from the skull by a bone called the
quadrate bone.   Among men and other mammals
the lower jaw is joined directly to the skull, the
quadrate bone becoming, in the vicissitudes of
evolution, the hammer (malleus) of the mammalian
ear.   Man has a four-chambered heart—two reser-
voirs which receive, and two pumps which propel,
the scarlet waters of the body.   Fishes have two-
chambered hearts; frogs and most reptiles have
three-chambered hearts; all mammals and birds

have four-chambered hearts. The red corpuscles in the blood of fishes, frogs, reptiles, and birds, are discs, double-convex, nucleated, and in shape oval or triangular. In man and in all other mammals (except the archaic camel) the red corpuscles are double-concave, non-nucleated, and circular. Man has a diaphragm dividing the body cavity into chest and abdomen, and a shining white bridge of interlacing fibres, called *corpus callosum*, uniting his cerebral hemispheres. And man is a mammal because, like other mammals, he has, in addition to the qualities already mentioned, these valuable and distinct characteristics.

IV. Man a Primate.

Man is a *primate*. There are four divisions in the order of primates—lemurs, monkeys, apes, and men. But the most interesting and important of these, according to man, is man. Man is a primate because, like other primates, he has arms and hands instead of fore-legs. And these are important characteristics. It was a splendid moment when the tendencies of evolution, pondering the possibilities of structural improvement, decided to rear the vertebrate upon its hind-limbs, and convert its anterior appendages into instruments of manipulation. So long as living creatures were able simply to move through the airs and waters of the earth and over the surface of the solids, they were powerless to modify the universe about them very much. But the moment beings were developed with parts of their bodies fitted to take hold of and move and fashion and compel the universe around them, that moment the life process was endowed with the power of miracles. With the invention of hands and arms commenced seriously that long campaign against the tendencies of inanimate nature which finds its most marvellous achievements in the sustained and triumphant operations of human industry. None of the primates excepting man use their hind-limbs as a sole means of changing their place in the universe, but in all of them the fore-limbs are regularly used as organs of manipulation. Man is a primate because his fingers and toes, like those of other primates (except the tiny marmosets of Brazil), end in nails. Man has neither claws to burrow into the earth, talons with which to hold and rend his victims, nor hoofs to put thunder into his movements. The human stomach, like that of all the other primates, is a bagpipe. The stomach of the carnivora is usually a simple sack, while rodents have, as a rule, two stomachs, and ruminants four. Man is a primate because his milk glands are located on the breast and are two in number. The mammary glands vary in number in the different orders of mammals, from two in the horse and whale to twenty-two in some insectivora. Most ruminating animals have four, swine ten, and carnivora generally six or eight. These glands may be located in the region of the groin, as in the horse and whale; between the fore-limbs, as in the elephant and bat; or arranged in pairs extending from the fore to the hind limbs, as in the carnivora and swine. In man and all other primates (except lemurs) the mammary glands are pectoral and two in number. All primates, including man, have also a disc-shaped placenta. The placenta is the organ of nutrition in mammalian embryos. It is found in all young-bearing animals above the marsupials, and consists of a mass of glands between the embryo and the parental body. In some animals it entirely surrounds and encloses the embryo; in others it assumes the form of a girdle; and in still others it is bell-shaped. The primates are the only animals in which this peculiar organ is in the shape of a simple disc.*

The nearest relatives by blood man has in this world are the exceedingly man-like apes — the tailless anthropoids—the gorillas and chimpanzees of Africa, and the orangs and gibbons of southern and insular Asia. The fact that man is an actual relative and descendant of the ape is one of the most disagreeable of the many distasteful truths which the human mind in its evolution has come upon. To a vanity puffed, as is that of human beings, to the splitting, the consanguinity of gorilla and gentleman seems horrible. Man prefers to have arrived on the earth by way of a ladder let down by his imagination from the celestial concave. Within his own memory man has been

---

* The bat and a few other animals have a disc-like placenta, but it develops into the disc shape by a different route from what it does in the primates.

guilty of many foolish and disgraceful things. But this attempt by him to repudiate his ancestors by surreptitiously fabricating for himself an origin different from, and more glorious than, the rest is one of the most absurd and scandalous in the whole list. It is a shallow logic—the logic of those who, without worth of their own, try to shine with a false and stolen lustre. No more masterly rebuke was ever administered to those in the habit of sneering at the truth in this matter than the caustic reply of Huxley to the taunt of the fat-witted Bishop—that he would rather be the descendant of a respectable ape than the descendant of one who not only closed his eyes to the facts around him, but used his official position to persuade others to do likewise. Man's reluctance to take his anatomical place beside his simian kinspeople has been exceeded only by his selfish and high-handed determination to exclude all other terrestrial beings from his heaven.

Man is a talkative and religious ape. He is an ape, but with a much greater amount of enterprise and with a greater likelihood of being found in every variety of climate. Like the anthropoid, man has a bald face and an obsolete tail. But he is distinguished from his arboreal relative by his arrogant bearing, his skilled larynx, and especially by the satisfaction he experiences in the contemplation of the image which appears when he looks in a mirror.

The man-like apes are from three to six feet tall, and are all of them very strong, the gorilla, who sometimes weighs over three hundred pounds, being about the bravest and most formidable unarmed animal on the planet. They are erect or semi-erect, have loud voices, plantigrade feet, and irritable dispositions—in all of these particulars being strikingly like men. The gorilla, chimpanzee, and gibbon are highlanders, preferring the uplands and mountains. The orang is a lowlander, living phlegmatically among the sylvan swamps of Sumatra and Borneo. The gorilla and chimpanzee are terrestrial, seldom going among the trees except to get food or to sleep. The orang and gibbon are arboreal, seldom coming to the ground except to drink or bathe. They all walk on their hind-limbs, generally in a stooping posture, with their knuckles or fingers touching the ground. But they sometimes walk with their arms hanging down by their sides, and sometimes with their hands clasped back of their heads to give them balance. None of them ever place their palms on the ground when they walk—that is, none of them walk on four feet. The anthropoid races, in the shape of their heads and faces and in the general form and structure of their bodies, and even in their habits of life, resemble in a remarkable manner the lowest races of human beings. This resemblance is recognised by the negro races, who call the gorilla and chimpanzee 'hairy men,' and believe them to be descendants of outcast members of their own species.

There are differences in structure between man and the apes, just as there are differences in structure between the Caucasian and the Caffre, or even between individual Caucasians or individual Caffres. There are differences in structure and topography, often very noticeable differences, even among members of the same family. But in all of its essential characters, and extending often to astonishing particulars, the structure of man is identical with that of the anthropoid (1).*

In external appearances the man-like races differ from men in having a luxuriant covering of natural hair. But anthropoids differ very much among themselves in this particular. The orang, usually covered with long hair, is sometimes almost hairless. There are, too, races of human beings whose bodies are covered with a considerable growth of hair. The Todas (Australians) and Ainus (aborigines of Japan) are noted for the hairiness of their bodies, certain individuals among them being covered with a real fur, especially on the lower limbs (2).

Individuals also often appear in every race with a remarkable development of the hair. Adrian and his son Fedor, exhibited years ago over Europe as 'dog-men,' are examples. The father was completely covered with a thick growth of fine dirty-yellow hair two or three inches long. Long tufts grew out of his nostrils and ears, giving him a striking resemblance to a Skye terrier. Fedor, and also his sister, were covered with hair like the

* Figures in parentheses ( ) at the close of borrowed ideas refer to book numbers in the bibliography at the close of the chapter.

father, but another son was like ordinary men. The man-like races have also longer arms in proportion to the height of the body than man generally has. But this is also true of human infants and negroes. The gibbon has relatively much longer arms than the other anthropoids. It differs from the chimpanzee in this respect more than the chimpanzee differs from man. When standing upright and reaching down with the middle finger, the gibbon can touch its foot, while the chimpanzee can reach only to the knee. Man ordinarily reaches part way down the thigh, but negroes have been known to have arms reaching to the knee-pan (3).

The skeleton of the African races contains many characters recognised by osteologists as ' pithecoid,' or ape-like. It is massive, the flat bones are thick, and the pelvis narrow. In the manlike apes the large toe is opposable to the other four, and is used by them much as the thumb is used. But this difference between the two races of beings is just what might be expected from the differences in their modes of life. Man has little need of this opposability on account of his exclusively terrestrial life, while to the ape it is indispensable on account of his arboreal environment and life. ' But there are,' says Haeckel, ' wild tribes of men who can oppose the large toe to the other four just as if it were a thumb, and even new-born infants of the most highly-developed races of men can grasp as easily with their hind-hands as with their forehands. Chinese boatmen row with their feet, and Bengal workmen weave with them. The negro, in whom the big toe is freely movable, seizes hold of the branches of trees with it when climbing, just like the four-handed apes' (4).

Many men have lost their arms by accident and have learned to use their feet as hands with wonderful skill. Not many years ago there died in Europe an armless violinist who had during his lifetime played to cultured audiences in most of the capitals of the world. Some of the most accomplished of penmen hold their pen between their toes. The man-like apes live to about the same age as man, and all of them, like man, have beards. The anthropoid beard, too, like the human, appears at the age of sexual maturity. The human beard often differs in colour from the hair of the scalp, and whenever it does it has been observed to be invariably lighter — never darker—than the hair on the scalp. This is true among all races of men. The same rule and the same uniformity exists among anthropoids. The races of mankind are divided into two primary groups depending upon the shape of the head and the character of the hair : the short-headed races (Brachycephali), such as the Malays, Mongols, and Aryans, with round or oval faces, straight hair, and vertical profiles ; and the long-headed races (Dolichocephali), with woolly hair and progna-thous faces, such as the Papuans and African races. The skin of the short-headed races is orange or white, while the skin and hair of the long-headed races are glossy black.

It is, at least, interesting that the orang and gibbon, who live in Asia and its islands, where the brachycephalic races of men supposedly arose, are themselves brachycephalic ; and that the gorilla and chimpanzee, who live in Africa, where the dolichocephalic races chiefly live, are dolichocephalic. The gorilla and chimpanzee also have, like the men and women of Africa, black skin and hair; while the hair of the orang is a reddish-brown, and its skin sometimes yellowish-white. The dentition of the anthropoids and men is in all essentials identical. They all have two sets of teeth : a set of milk-teeth, twenty in number, and thirty-two permanent teeth, the permanents consisting of two incisors, one canine, two premolars, and three molars, in each half-jaw. Man has ordinarily twelve pairs of ribs and thirty-two vertebræ. So has the orang. The other anthropoids have thirteen pairs of ribs. But the number of ribs in both human and anthropoid beings is not uniform, man occasionally having thirteen pairs, and the gorilla fourteen. Man has also the same number of caudal vertebræ in his rudimentary tail as the anthropoid has. The hands and feet of anthropoids, bone for bone and muscle for muscle, correspond with those of men, no greater structural differences existing than among different species of men. The human foot has three muscles not found in the human hand — a short flexor muscle, a short extensor muscle, and a long muscle extending from the fibula to the foot. All of these muscles are found in the anthropoid foot just as in the foot of man. There are also the same differences between the arrangement of the bones of the anthropoid wrist and ankle as between the wrist and ankle bones of man. Whatever set of anatomical particulars may be selected, whether it be hands, arms, feet, muscles, skull, viscera, ribs, or dentition, it is found that the anthropoid races and men are in all essentials the same. The differences are such as have arisen as a result of different modes of life, and such as exist between different tribes of either group of animals.

'The structural differences which separate man from the gorilla and chimpanzee,' says Huxley, in summing up the conclusion of his brilliant inquiry into 'Man's Place in Nature,' 'are not so great as those which separate the gorilla from the lower apes.'

'The body of man and that of the anthropoid are not only peculiarly similar,' says Haeckel, 'but they are practically one and the same in every important respect. The same two hundred bones, in the same order and structure, make up our inner skeleton ; the same three hundred muscles effect our movements ; the same hair clothes our skin ; the same four-chambered heart is the central pulsometer in our circulation ; the same thirty-two teeth are set in the same order in our jaws ; the same salivary, hepatic, and gastric glands compass our digestion ; the same reproductive organs insure the maintenance of our race ' (5).

' Not being able,' says Owen in his paper on
' The Characters of Mammalia,' ' to appreciate or
conceive of the distinction between the psychical
phenomena of a chimpanzee and of a Boschisman
or of an Aztec with arrested brain-growth, as
being of a nature so essential as to preclude a
comparison between them, or as being other than
a difference in degree, I cannot shut my eyes to
the significance of that all-pervading similitude of
structure—every tooth, every bone, strictly homologous—which makes the determination of the
difference between *Homo* and *Pithecus* the anato-
mist's difficulty.'

' If before the appearance of man on the earth,'
says Ward in his ' Dynamic Sociology,' ' an
imaginary painter had visited it, and drawn a
portrait embodying the thorax of the gibbon, the
hands and feet of the gorilla, the form and skull
of the chimpanzee, the brain development of the
orang, and the countenance of *Semnopithecus*, giving
to the whole the average stature of all of these apes,
the result would have been a being not far removed
from our conception of the primitive man, and not
widely different from the actual condition of
certain low tribes of savages. The brain development would perhaps be too low for the average
of any existing tribe, and would correspond better
with that of certain microcephalous idiots and
cretins, of which the human race furnishes many
examples.'

And it is not true, as is commonly supposed,
that, after all other resemblances between the

human and anthropoid structures have been made out, there still exists somewhere some undistinguishable difference in the organic structure of their brains. All differences in structure from time to time suspected or asserted to exist between the brain of man and that of the man-like apes have been one after another completely swept away. And it is now known to all neurologists that the human and anthropoid brains differ structurally in no particulars whatever, both of them containing the same lobes, the same ventricles and cornua, and the same convolutional outline. Even the posterior lobe, the posterior cornu, and the hippocampus minor, so long triumphantly asserted to be characteristic features of the human brain, have been pitilessly identified in all anthropoids by the profound and terrible Huxley. There is not an important fold or fissure in the brain of man that is not found in the brain of the anthropoid. 'The surface of the brain of a monkey,' says Huxley, 'exhibits a sort of skeleton map of man's, and in the man-like apes the details become more and more filled in, until it is only in minor characters that the chimpanzee's or the orang's brain can be structurally distinguished from man's ' (6).

The great difference physically between man and the anthropoids, aside from man's talented larynx and erect posture, lies in man's abnormal cranial capacity. The normal human cranium never contains less than 55 cubic inches of space, while the largest gorilla cranium contains only $34\frac{1}{2}$ cubic inches. This is a difference of $20\frac{1}{2}$ cubic inches. And 20½ cubic inches of thinking matter is an alarming amount to be lacking in a single individual. But this cranial gap between gorilla and man is deprived of some of its significance by the fact that human crania sometimes measure 114 cubic inches, making a difference between the smallest and largest human brains of 59 cubic inches. The difference between the gorilla and the savage in cranial capacity is, therefore, *only about one-third as great as the cranial chasm between the savage and the sage.*

V. Recapitulation.

The anatomical gulf between men and apes does not exist. There are, in fact, no gulfs anywhere, only gradations. All chasms are completely covered by unmistakable affinities, in spite of the fact that the remains of so many millions of deceased races lie hidden beneath seas or everlastingly locked in the limy bosoms of the continents. There are closer kinships and remoter kinships, but there are kinships everywhere. The more intimate kinships are indicated by more definite and detailed similarities, and the more general relationships by more fundamental resemblances. All creatures are bound to all other creatures by the ties of a varying but undeniable consanguinity.

Man stands unquestionably in the primate order of animals, because he has certain qualities of structure which all primates have, and which all other animals have not : hands and arms and nails, a bagpipe stomach, great subordination of the cerebellum, a disc-like placenta, teeth differentiated into incisors, canines, and molars, and pectoral milk glands.

Man is more closely akin to the anthropoid apes than to the other primates on account of his immense brain, his ape-like face, his vertical spine, and in being a true two-handed biped. The man-like apes and men have the same number and kinds of teeth, the same limb bones and muscles, like ribs and vertebræ, an atrophied tail, the same brain structure, and a suspicious similarity in looks and disposition. Men and anthropoids live about the same number of years, both being toothless and wrinkled in old age. The beard, too, in both classes of animals appears at the same period of life and obeys the same law of variation in colour. Even the hairs on different parts of the bodies of men and anthropoids, as on the arms, incline at a like angle to the body surface. The hair on the upper arm and that on the forearm, in both anthropoids and men, point in opposite directions—toward the elbow. This peculiarity is found nowhere in the animal kingdom excepting in a few American monkeys.

Man's mammalian affinities are shown in his diaphragm, his hair, his four-chambered heart, his *corpus callosum*, his non-nucleated blood-corpuscles, and his awkward incubation.

The fishes, frogs, reptiles, birds, and non-human mammals are human in having two body cavities, segmented internal skeletons, two pairs of limbs, skulls and spinal columns, red blood, brains, and dorsal cords; and in possessing two eyes, two ears, nostrils, and mouth opening out of the head.

And finally all animals, including man, are related to all other animal forms by the great underlying facts of their origin, structure, composition, and destiny. All creatures, whether they live in the sea, in the heavens, or in subterranean glooms; whether they swim, fly, crawl, or walk; whether their world is a planet or a water-drop; and whether they realise it or not, commence existence in the same way, are composed of the same substances, are nourished by the same matters, follow fundamentally the same occupations, all do under the circumstances the best they can, and all arrive ultimately at the same pitiful end.

VI. The Meaning of Homology.

The similarities and homologies of structure existing between man and other animals, and between other animals and still others, are not accidental and causeless. They are not resemblances scattered arbitrarily among the multitudinous forms of life by the capricious levities of chance. That all animals commence existence as an egg and are all made up of cells composed of the same protoplasmic substance, and all inhale oxygen and exhale carbon dioxide, and are all seeking pleasure and seeking to avoid pain, are more than ordinary facts. They are filled with inferences. That vertebrate animals, differing in externals as widely as herring and Englishmen, are all built

according to the same fundamental plan, with
marrow-filled backbones and exactly two pairs of
limbs branching in the same way, is an astonishing
coincidence. That the wing of the bird, the fore-
leg of the dog, the flipper of the whale, and the
fore-limb of the toad and crocodile, have essentially
the same bones as the human arm has is a fact
which may be without significance to blind men,
but to no one else. The metamorphosis of the
frog from a fish, of the insect from a worm, and of
a poet from a senseless cell, are transformations
simply marvellous in meaning. And it is not
easy, since Darwin, to understand how such lessons
could remain long unintelligible, even to stones
and simpletons. Not many generations have
passed, however, since these revelations, now so
distinct and wonderful, fell on the listless minds
of men as ineffectually as the glories of the flower
fall on the sightless sockets of the blind.

It is hardly two generations since the highest
intelligences on the earth conceived that not
only the different varieties of men—the black, the
white, and the orange—but all the orders and
genera of the animal world, and not only animals,
but plants, had all been somehow simultaneously
and arbitrarily brought into existence in some
indistinct antiquity, and that they had from the
beginning all existed with practically the same
features and in approximately the same conditions
as those with which and in which they are found
to-day. The universe was conceived to be a fixed
and stupid something, born as we see it, incapable

of growth, and indulging in nothing but repetitions. There were no necessary coherencies and consanguinities, no cosmical tendencies operating eternally and universally. All was whimsical and arbitrary. It was not known that anything had grown or evolved. All things were believed to have been given beginning and assigned to their respective places in the universe by a potential and all-clever creator. The serpent was limbless because it had officiously allowed Eve to include in her dietary that which had been expressly forbidden. The quadruped walked with its face towards the earth as a structural reminder of its subjection to the biped, who was supposed to be especially skilled in keeping his eyes rolled heavenward. The flowers flung out their colours, not for the benefit of the bugs and bees, and the stars paraded, not because they were moved to do so by their own eternal urgings, but because man had eyes capable of being affected by them. Man was an erect and featherless vertebrate because his hypothetical maker was erect and featherless. (I wonder whether, if a clam should conceive a creator, it would have the magnanimity to make him an insect or a vertebrate, or anything other than a great big clam.)

VII. The Earth an Evolution.

The world now knows—at least, the scientific part of it knows—that these things are not true, that they are but the solemn fancies of honest but simple-minded ancients who did the best they could in that twilight age to explain to their inquiring instincts the wilderness of phenomena in which they found themselves. The universe is a process. It is not petrified, but flowing. It is going somewhere. Everything is changing and evolving, and will always continue to do so. The forms of life, of continents and oceans, and of streams and systems, which we perceive as we open our senses upon the world to-day, are not the forms that have always existed, and they are not the forms of the eternal future. There was a time, away in the inconceivable, when there was no life upon the earth, no solids, and no seas. The world was an incandescent lump, lifeless and alone, in the cold solitudes of the spaces. There was a time—there *must* have been a time—when life appeared for the first time upon the earth, simple cellules without bones or blood, and without a suspicion of their immense and quarrelsome posterity. There was a time when North America was an island, and the Alleghany Mountains were the only mountains of the continent. The time was—in the coal-forming age—when the Mississippi Valley, from the Colorado Islands to the Alleghanies, was a vast marsh or sea, choked with forests of equisetum and fern, and swarming with gigantic reptiles now extinct. There was a time when palms grew in Dakota, and magnolias waved in the semi-tropical climate of Greenland and Spitzbergen. There was a time when there were no Rocky Mountains in existence, no Andes, no Alps, no Pyrenees, and no Himalayas. And that time, compared with the vast stretches of geological duration, was not so very long ago, for these mountains are all young mountains. The time was when Jurassic saurians—those repulsive ruffians of that rude old time—represented the highest intelligence and civilisation of the known universe. There were no men and women in the world, not even savages, when our ape-like forefathers wandered and wondered through the awesome silences of primeval wilds; there were no railroads, steamboats, telegraphs, telephones, typewriters, harvesters, electric lights, nor sewing machines; no billionaires nor bicycles, no socialists nor steam-heat, no 'watered stock' nor 'government by injunction,' no women's clubs, captains of industry, labour unions, nor 'yellow perils'—there was none of these things on the earth a hundred years ago. All things have evolved to be what they are—the continents, oceans, and atmospheres, and the plants and populations that live in and upon them.

There will come a time, too, looking forward into the future, when what we see now will be seen no more. As we go backward into the past, the earth in all of its aspects rapidly changes; the continents dwindle, the mountains melt, and existing races and species disappear one after another. The farther we penetrate into the past, the stranger and the more different from the present does everything become, until finally we come to a world of molten rocks and vapourised seas without a creeping thing upon it. As it has been in the past so will it be in time to come. The present is not everlasting. The minds that perceive upon this planet a thousand centuries in the future will perceive a very different world from that which the minds of this day perceive— different arts, animals, events, ideals, geographies, sciences, and civilisations. The earth seems fixed and changeless because we are so fleeting. We see it but a moment, and are gone. The tossing forest in the wrath of the storm is motionless when looked at by a flash of lightning. The same tendencies that have worked past changes are at work to-day as tirelessly as in the past. By invisible chisels the mountains are being sculptured, ocean floors are lifting, and continents are sinking into the seas. Species, systems, and civilisations are changing, some crumbling and passing away, others rising out of the ruins of the departed. Mighty astronomical tendencies are secretly but relentlessly at work, and immense vicissitudes are in store for this clod of our nativity. The earth is doomed to be frozen to death. In a few million years, according to astronomers, the sun will have shrunken to a fraction of his present size, and will have become correspondingly reduced in heat-giving powers. It is estimated that in twelve or fifteen million years the sun, upon whose mighty dispensations all life and activity on the earth are absolutely dependent, will become so enfeebled that no form of life on the earth will be possible. The partially-cooled earth itself is giving up its internal warmth, and will continue to give it up until it is the same temperature as the surrounding abysms, which is the frightful negative of something like 270 centigrade degrees. These are not very cheerful facts for those who inhabit the earth to contemplate. But they that seek the things that cheer must seek another sphere. No power can stay the emaciation of suns or the thievery of enveloping immensities. Old age is inevitable. It is far off, but it is as certain as human decay, and as mournful. In that dreadful but inevitable time no living being will be left in this world; there will be no cities nor states nor vanities nor creeping things, no flowers, no twilights, no love, only a frozen sphere. The oceans that now rave against the rocky flanks of the continents will be locked in eternal immobility; the atmospheres, which to-day drive their fleecy flocks over the azure meads of heaven and float sweet sounds and feathered forms, will be, in that terrible time, turned to stone; the radiant woods and fields, the home of the myriads and the green play-places of the shadows, will, like all that live, move, and breathe, have rotted into the everlasting lumber of the elements. There will be no Europe then, no pompous philosophies, no hellish rich, and no gods. All will have suffered indescribable refrigeration. The earth will be a fluidless, lifeless, sunless cinder, unimaginably dead and desolate, a decrepit and pitiful old ruin falling endlessly among heartless immensities, the universal tomb of the activities.

The universe is an evolution. Change is as extensive as time and space. The present has come out of that which has been, and will enter into and determine that which is to be. Everything has a biography. Everything has evolved—*everything*—from the murmur on the lips of the speechless babe to the soul of the poet, and from the molecule to Jehovah.

VIII. The Factors of Organic Evolution.

The animal kingdom represents one of the two grand branches of the organic universe. It has been evolved—evolved in a manner as simple and straightforward as it is revolting. It has all been brought about by *partiality* or *selection*. Generations of beings have come into existence. The individual members of each generation have differed from each other—differed in size, strength, speed, colour, shape, sagacity, luck, and likelihood of life. No two beings, not even those born from the same womb, are in all respects identical. Hardships have come. They have come from the inanimate universe in the form of floods, fires, frosts, accidents, diseases, droughts, storms, and the like; from other species, who were competitors or enemies; and from unbrotherly members of the same species. Some have survived, but the great majority have perished. Only a fraction, and generally an appallingly small fraction, of each generation of a species have lived to maturity. The lobster lays 10,000 eggs in a season, yet the mortality is such that the number of lobsters do not increase from one year to another. The elephant is the slowest breeder of all animals, yet, if they should all live, the offspring of a single pair in 750 years would, according to Darwin, number nearly 19,000,000. It has been shown that at the normal rate of increase of English sparrows, if none were to die save of old age, it would take but twenty years for a single pair to give one sparrow to every square inch in the State of Indiana (7). A single cyclops (one of the humbler crustaceans) may have 5,000,000 descendants in a season. One aphis will produce 100 young, and these young will reproduce in like manner for ten generations in a season, when, if they should all live, there would be a quintillion of young. A female white ant, when adult, does nothing but lie in a cell and lay eggs. She lays 80,000 eggs a day regularly for several months. An oyster lays 2,000,000 eggs in a season, and if all these eggs came to maturity a few dozen oysters might supply the markets of the world. The tapeworm is said to produce the incredible number of 1,000,000,000 ova, and some of the humbler plants three times this number of spores. If each egg of the codfish should produce an adult, a single pair in twenty-five years would produce a mass of fish larger than the earth. Lower forms of life are even more prolific than the higher. Maupas said that certain microscopic infusorians which he studied multiplied so rapidly that, if they should continue to multiply for thirty-eight days, and all of them should live, any one of them would produce a mass of protoplasm as big as the sun.

Those of each generation that have died have been inferior, or unfitted to the environment in which they found themselves. Those that have survived have been superior, superior in something — bigness, cunning, courage, virtue, vitality, strength, speed, littleness, or ferocity— something that has related them advantageously to surrounding conditions. The surviving remnant of each generation have become the progenitors of the next generation, and have transmitted, or tended to transmit, to their offspring the qualities of their superiority. This winnowing has gone on in each generation of living beings during many millions of years—almost ever since life commenced to be on the earth. Some have continued themselves, and others have died childless. The environment of each species has been an immense sieve, and only the superior have gone through it. Different environments have emphasised different qualities of structure and disposition, and have thus given rise to permanent varieties in survival. These varieties, through the accumulated effects of many generations of selection, have diverged into species; species, after a still longer series of selections, have evolved into genera; genera have evolved into families; families into orders; and so on. In this simple, terrible manner have all the branches of organic beings (thanks to the horrors of a million ages) been brought into existence.

Variation, therefore, which furnishes variety in

offspring; *Heredity*, which tends to perpetuate peculiarities by causing offspring to resemble more or less the characters of their parents; and *Environment*, which determines the character of the selections, are the three factors, and the only three factors, in organic evolution.

IX. The Evidences of Organic Evolution.

That the forms of life to-day found on the earth have come into existence by the evolution of the more complex forms from the simpler, and of these simpler forms from still simpler, through the ever-operating law of Selection, is a necessary conclusion from the following facts:

1. The existence in the animal world of all grades of structures, from the humblest possible protozoan, whose body consists of a single simple speck, to the most powerful and complex of mammals. There are estimated to be something like a million species of animals living on the earth to-day. There may be several times this number. These species are linked together by millions of varieties, and are so related to each other that they may be all gathered together into various genera; these genera may be grouped into families, the families into orders, and the orders into seven or eight great primary phyla. By taking existing species and adding to them the extinct species of the rocks, and placing them all according to their structural affinities, it is possible to arrange them in the form of a tree with the various phyla, orders, families, genera, and

species, branching and rebranching from the main trunk. The existence of structures, so graduated as to render such an arrangement possible, is in itself suggestive of a common relationship and origin.

2. Evolution is suggested by the similarities and homologies of structure found throughout the animal kingdom. Some of these similarities and homologies have already been mentioned. They are everywhere—remoter and more fundamental, some of them, others closer and more detailed. To the untrained mind, which sees surfaces only, and not even surfaces well, the animal world is an interminable miscellany of forms. But to the biologist, who looks deeper and with immense acumen over the whole field of animal life, there are only seven or eight different types of structure in the entire animal world. These seven or eight types correspond with the primary classes, or phyla, into which animals are divided, viz., protozoa, sponges, celenterates, echinoderms, worms, mollusks, arthropods, and vertebrates. However widely the members of each of these great groups may differ among themselves in colour, size, habits of life, and the like, the members of each group all resemble each other fundamentally. Moles differ from monkeys, bats from men, and birds from crocodiles and toads. They differ enormously. But they are all vertebrates with red blood, double body cavities, backbones, two pairs of limbs, and five fingers on each limb. When they are looked at superficially, there is

not much similarity between a water-strider and a butterfly or between a stag-beetle and a gnat. But they are all, in reality, built according to the same plan. Like all other insects, they have six legs, a sheath-like skeleton, and bodies characteristically divided into head, thorax, and abdomen. It is the same with all other great classes of beings. All worms resemble each other; and so do all mollusks, although they may differ in particulars as widely as nautiluses and clams. Echinoderms have a radiate structure, celenterates and sponges are vase-like in shape, and protozoa are one-celled. The differences in structure among the members of a group consist in different modifications of a fundamental type. Among the vertebrates the fore-limb may be an arm, a leg, a wing, a shovel, a flipper, or a fin. But in all cases it is the same organ—that is, the same implement modified to serve different ends. Take the mouth-parts of insects. In the grasshopper and cricket these parts are fitted for grinding; in the moths and butterflies they are fashioned into long tubes for sucking the sweets of flowers; in the mosquito they form an elaborate apparatus for drilling and drinking; and in the mayfly the mouth-parts, though present, are not used at all. In all of these animals these parts are essentially the same, although differing so much in their forms and purposes that the unscientific can scarcely be made to believe they are fundamentally alike. There is no fact more familiar to the biologist or more frequently met with in the fields of animal morphology than the fact that the same general type may be hammered into dozens, or hundreds, or even thousands, of different patterns by the incessant industry of its surroundings, and that the same organic part may be moulded into various implements serving totally different ends by the environmental vicissitudes of time and space. On the hypothesis that the members of each group of animals possessing common characteristics, whether the group be large or small, have sprung from a common ancestry, and that the differences in structure have arisen as a result of differences in environment, the similarities and homologies of structure existing among animals are perfectly intelligible. But on any other supposition they are inexplicable.

3. Evolution is suggested by the remarkable series of phenomena presented by embryology. There are at least four facts in the developmental history of every creature which can hardly be accounted for on any other supposition than that of organic evolution.

First, the fact that every animal, above the lowest, individually passes through an evolution between the beginning of its existence and its maturity. Terrestrial beings are not born, like Minerva, full-grown. They grow. They evolve. They commence close down to the very atoms. And from this lowly genesis they rise, through a series of marvellous changes, to that high state of perfection and greatness from which they descend to dissolution.

If we knew by actual observation as little concerning the evolution of individuals as we do of the evolution of species—if we had always been used to seeing animals, including ourselves, in full bloom—had never watched the tadpole, the pupa, and the babe pass through their wonderful metamorphoses on their way to maturity, it would probably be just as hard for many minds to believe that animals evolve individually to be what they are as it is for them to believe that species have grown to be what they are. In the case of individuals, however, the evolution takes place right before our eyes largely, while the evolution of species goes on so slowly and stretches back so far into the past that it can only be inferred.

Second, the fact that animals, no matter how much they may differ from each other at maturity, all begin existence at the same place. Every animal commences its organic existence as an egg —as a one-celled animal—as an organism identical in structure with the simplest protozoan. The ova of whales ' are no larger than fern seeds.' The eggs of the coral, the crab, the ape, and the man are so precisely alike that the highest powers of the microscope cannot distinguish between them.

Third, the fact that the members of the same great group of animals in their individual development pass through similar stages of evolution. The ' worm ' stage in the development of most insects and the ' fish ' stage of frogs are well known.

There are no more remarkable instances of individual evolution in the whole range of animal life. The fish, the reptile, the bird, the dog, and the human being—all vertebrates, in short—cannot for some time after their embryonic commencement be distinguished from each other. ' The feet of lizards and mammals, the wings and feet of birds, and the hands and feet of men,' says the illustrious Von Baer, as quoted by Darwin, ' all arise from the same fundamental form ' (8).

' It is quite in the later stages of development,' says Huxley, ' that the human being presents marked differences from the ape, while the latter departs as much from the dog in its development as the man does' (6).

Not only frogs, but reptiles, birds, and mammals, including man, all have gills at a certain stage in their embryonic development. Nearly all the lower invertebrate animals are hermaphroditic—that is, in the body of each animal is found the two kinds of sex organs which in the higher animals exist in distinct animals. And frogs, birds, and other higher animals, which as adults are unisexual, have, as an inheritance from these primitive forms, hermaphroditic embryos (10).

Fourth, the fact that the structural stages through which animals in embryo pass correspond in a wonderful manner with the permanent structures of those lower forms which extend serially back to the beginnings of life. It is the proudest boast of the embryologist that he is able to know the route through which any species has come to be what it is by a simple study of the individual evolution of its members. Each animal repeats in its individual evolution the evolution of its species. This recapitulation is not always complete—is, in fact, frequently vague, sometimes circuitous, and often broken or abbreviated. Processes requiring originally centuries or thousands of years to accomplish are here telescoped into a few months, or even days. It is not strange that the process is imperfect. But so firmly is the belief in the correspondence of ontogeny and phylogeny fixed in the minds of modern biologists that, in determining the classification and affinities of any particular animal, more reliance is placed on the facts of embryology than on those of adult structure.

The first thing that an animal becomes after it is an egg—unless it is a one-celled animal, in which case it remains always an egg—is two cells; these two cells become four; these four become eight; and so on, until the embryo becomes a many-celled ball, consisting of a single layer of cells surrounding a fluid interior. A dimple forms in the cell layer on one side of this ball, and, by deepening to a hollow, changes the ball into a double-walled sac. This is the *gastrula*—the permanent structure of the sponges and celenterates, and an (almost) invariable stage in the larval development of all animals above the sponges and celenterates. The gastrula becomes a worm (or an insect or a fish through the worm) by elongation and enlargement, and by the development of the endoderm, which is the inner layer of the cell wall, into organs of nutrition and reproduction, and by the development of the ectoderm, which is the outer cell layer, into organs of motion and sensation.

The embryonic development of a human being is not different in kind from the embryonic development of any other animal. Every human being at the beginning of his organic existence is a protozoan, about $\frac{1}{125}$ inch in diameter; at another stage of development he is a tiny sac-shaped mass of cells without blood or nerves, the gastrula; at another stage he is a worm, with a pulsating tube instead of a heart, and without head, neck, spinal column, or limbs; at another stage he has, as a backbone, a rod of cartilage extending along the back, and a faint nerve cord, as in amphioxus, the lowest of the vertebrates; at another stage he is a fish with a two-chambered heart, mesonephric kidneys, and gill-slits with gill arteries leading to them, just as in fishes; at another stage he is a reptile with a three-chambered heart, and voiding his excreta through a cloaca like other reptiles; and finally, when he enters upon post-natal sins and actualities, he is a sprawling, squalling, unreasoning quadruped. The human larva from the fifth to the seventh month of development is covered with a thick growth of hair and has a true caudal appendage, like the monkey. At this stage the embryo has in all thirty-eight vertebræ, nine of which are caudal, and the great toe extends at right angles to the other toes, and is not longer than the other toes, but shorter, as in the ape.

These facts are unmistakable. There is a reason for everything, and there is a reason for these transformations through which each generation of living beings journeys. The individual passes through them because the species to which he belongs has passed through them. They represent ancestral wanderings. As if to emphasise the kinship of all of life's forms and to render incontrovertible the fact of universal evolution, Nature compels every individual to commence existence at the same place, and to recapitulate in his individual evolution the phylogenetic journeyings of his species.

4. That existing forms of life have been evolved from other forms, and that these ancestral forms have been different from those derived from them, is shown by the occasional appearance of antecedent and abandoned types of structure among the offspring of existing species. Occasionally a human child is born strangely unlike its parents, but bearing an unmistakable resemblance in looks and disposition to his great-grandfather or some other remote ancestor. This is *atavism*, that tendency to revert to ancestral types which is prevalent among all animals. We may think of it figuratively as a flash of indecision when Nature hesitates for a moment whether to adopt a new form of structure or cling to the old and tried. Horses and mules are sometimes born with three toes on each foot, and zebra-like stripes on their legs and shoulders; and domestic pigeons, such as are naturally black, red, or mottled, occasionally produce offspring with blue plumage and two black

wing-bars, like the wild rock-dove, from which all domestic breeds have sprung. In man the cheek-bone and the frontal bone of the forehead consist normally each of a single bone. But in children and human embryos these bones are always double, as is normally the case in adults among some of the anthropoids and other mammals. Gills appear regularly in the embryos of reptiles, birds, and mammals, and human young are sometimes born with gill-slits on the neck. There are times when, owing to inaccurate or incomplete embryological development, these fish-like characteristics are so perfect at birth as to allow liquids, on being swallowed, to pass out through them and trickle down on the outside of the neck. Many muscles are occasionally developed in man which are normal in the apes and other mammals. As many as seven different muscular variations have been found in a single human being, every one of which were muscles found normally in the structure of the apes (8).

5. Closely akin to atavism, which is the occasional persistence of ancestral types of character, is the regular occurrence of vestigial organs or structures, organs which in ancestral forms have definite functions, but which in existing species, owing to changed conditions, are rudimentary and useless. On the back of each ankle of the horse are two splints, the atrophied remains of the second and fourth toes. Similar vestiges of two obsolete toes are also found just back of the wrists and ankles on all the two-toed ungulates, such as the

cow and sheep. In the body of the whale where hind-limbs would naturally be, there are found the anatomical ruins of these organs in the form of a few diminutive bones. The same thing is true in the sirenians. In the Greenland whale there are remnants of both femur and tibia in the region of the atrophied hind-limbs. The snakes are limbless, but the pythons and boas have internal remnants of hind-limbs, and sometimes even clawed structures representing toes. The so-called 'glass-snake' or 'joint-snake' (which is really a limbless lizard) has four complete internal limbs. Young turtles, parrots, and whalebone whales have teeth, but the adults of these animals are toothless. Cows, sheep, deer, and other ruminants, never have as adults any upper incisors, but these teeth are found in the fœtal stages of these animals just under the gums. The female frog has rudimentary male reproductive organs, and the male has corresponding vestiges of female organs. Similar remnants of the reproductive structures exist in many other animals. They represent stages in the transition from the hermaphroditism of primitive animals to the unisexuality of the higher forms, the separation of the sex organs into those of male and female having come about through the decay of one set of structures in each individual.

For reasons which it is not necessary to mention here, biologists believe that insects all originated from a common parental form, with two pairs of wings and six legs. Insects all retain their original allowance of legs, but in many species one or the other pair of wings has become more or less degenerated. In the whole order of flies the back pair of wings is represented by a couple of insignificant knobs. In the Strepsiptera, a sub-order of beetles, the front-wings are similarly reduced, being mere twisted filaments. Many parasites, such as fleas and ticks, whose mode of life renders organs of aerial locomotion unnecessary, are entirely wingless. The insects of small isolated islands are also largely without wings, the proportion of wingless species being much larger than among insects inhabiting continents. This is due to their greater liability on small land masses of being carried out to sea and drowned, owing to the feebleness and uncertainty of insect flight. On the island of Madeira, out of the 550 species found there, 220 species no longer have the power of flight.

Air-breathing animals — amphibians, reptiles, birds, and mammals—have normally a pair of lungs — a right one and a left one. But in snakes and snake-like lizards, where the body is very slender and elongated, only one lung, sometimes the right one, and sometimes the left, is fully developed. The right ovary is likewise aborted in all birds, the left one yielding all the eggs. The swifts and frigate birds live almost their whole lives long on the wing, and the legs of these birds have grown so short and weak and rudimentary, as a result of their constant life in the air, that they can scarcely walk. The chimney swift is said never to alight anywhere except on the sooty inner walls of the chimney where its nest is. Its food consists of insects which it gathers in the air, and the few dead twigs used in making its nest are nipped from the tree while the bird continues its flight. The ostriches, cassowaries, and many other birds, have, on the other hand, developed their legs at the expense of their wings. The ostrich is said to be able to outrun the horse, but it has no power of flight, although it has wings and wing muscles, and even the skin-folds covering the wings corresponding to those of birds that fly. But its whole flying apparatus is in ruins. The rudimentary hind-toe of birds is a vestigial organ, and so are the claws which appear on the thumb and first finger of all young birds. So also are the rudiments of eyes in cave crickets, fishes, and other inhabitants of total darkness. The flounder and other so-called flat fishes swim straight up, as ordinary fishes do, when young. But as they grow they incline more and more to one side, and finally swim entirely on their side, the eye on the lower side migrating around, and joining the other on the upper side of the head.

About the first thing a human infant does on coming into the world is to prove its arboreal origin by grasping and spitefully clinging to everything that stimulates its palms. A little peeperless babe an hour old can perform feats of strength with its hands and arms that many men and women cannot equal. It can support the entire weight of its body for several seconds hanging by its hands. Dr. Robinson, an English physician,

found as a result of sixty experiments on as many
infants, more than half of whom were less than an
hour old, that with two exceptions every babe was
able to hang to the finger or to a small stick, and
sustain the whole weight of the body for at least
ten seconds. Twelve of those just born held on
for nearly a minute. At the age of two or three
weeks, when this power is greatest, several succeeded in sustaining themselves for over a minute
and a half, two for over two minutes, and one for
two minutes and thirty-five seconds. The young
ape for some weeks after birth clings tenaciously
to its mother's neck and hair, and the instinct of
the child to cling to objects is probably a survival
of the instinct of the young ape. I believe it
is Wallace who relates somewhere an incident
which illustrates the instinct of the young simian
to cling to something. Wallace had captured
a young ape, and was carrying it to camp, when
the little fellow happened to get its hands on
the naturalist's whiskers, which it mistook, evidently, for the hirsute property of its mother,
and, driven by the powerful instinct of self-preservation, it hung on to them so desperately it
could scarcely be pulled loose. Many mammals
are provided with a well-developed muscular
apparatus for the manipulation of their ears. But
in man there does not exist the same necessity for
auricular detection of enemies, and while these
muscles still exist, and are capable of being used
to a slight extent by occasional individuals, they
are generally so emaciated as to be useless.

Another vestigial organ in the body of man, and one of significance from the standpoint of morphology, is the tail. The tail is an exceedingly unpopular part of the human anatomy, most men and women being unwilling to admit that they have such an appendage. But many a person who has hitherto dozed in ignorance on this matter has learned with considerable dismay, when he has for the first time looked upon the undraped lineaments of the human skeleton, that man actually has a tail. It consists of three or four (sometimes five) small vertebræ, more or less fused, at the posterior end of the spinal column. That this is really a rudimentary tail is proved beyond a doubt by the fact that in the embryo it is highly developed, being longer than the limbs, and is provided with a regular muscular apparatus for wagging it. These caudal muscles are generally represented in grown-up people by bands of fibrous tissue, but cases are known where the actual muscles have persisted through life (9).

The nictitating membrane, which in birds and many reptiles consists of a half-transparent curtain acting as a lid to sweep the eye, is in the human eye dwindled to a small membranous remnant, draped at the inner corner. The growth of hair over the human body surface may be regarded, in view of the sartorial habits of man, as a vestigial inheritance from hairy ancestors. One of the most notorious of the vestigial organs of man is the vermiform appendix, a small slender sac opening from the large intestine near where the large intestine is joined by the small intestine. In some animals this organ is large and performs an important part in the process of digestion. But in man it is a mere rudiment, not only of no possible aid in digestion, but the source of frequent disease, and even of death.

There are in all, according to Darwin, about eighty vestigial organs in the human body. But these organs occur everywhere throughout the animal kingdom. There is not an order of animals, nor of plants either, without them. They are necessary facts growing out of evolution. Organic structures are the result of adjustment to surrounding conditions. The continual changes in environment to which all organisms are exposed necessitate corresponding changes in structure. And the vestiges found in the bodies of all animals represent parts which in the previous existence were useful and necessary to a complete adjustment of the organism, but which, owing to a change of emphasis in surroundings, have become useless, and consequently shrunken. They are the obsolete or obsolescent parts of animal structure —parts which have been outgrown and superseded—the 'silent letters' of morphology. They sustain the same relation to the individual organism as dead or dwindling species sustain to a fauna. They furnish indisputable proof of the kinship and unity of the animal world.

6. It is only on the supposition that the life of the earth has evolved step by step with the evolution of the land masses, and that the forms of life

from which existing forms were evolved were dispersed over the earth at a time when physiographic conditions were very different from what they are now, that it is possible to account for the peculiar manner in which animals are distributed over the earth.   The cassowary is a flightless bird of the ostrich order inhabiting Australia and the islands to the north of it.   This bird is found nowhere else in the world, and each area has its own particular species.   The same things are also true of the kangaroo.   It is found over a similar region, with a different species occupying each land mass. Now, on the hypothesis of special creation there is no thinkable reason why these animals should be divided, as they are, into distinct species, and restricted to this particular region.   But on the hypothesis of evolution it is perfectly plain.   All of these regions at one time were united with one another, and were subsequently submerged in part, forming islands.   Each group of animals, being isolated from every other group and subjected to somewhat different conditions, developed a style of departure from the original type of structure different from that of every other group in response to the peculiar conditions operating upon it.   This has led, in the course of centuries of selection, to the formation of distinct species such as exist to-day.

Lombock Strait, a narrow neck of water between Bali and Lombock Island, and Macassar Strait, separating Celebes from Borneo, are parts of a continuous passage of water which in remote times separated two continents—an Indo-Malayan continent to which belonged Borneo, Sumatra, Java, and the Malay Peninsula; and an Austro-Malayan continent, now represented by Australia, Celebes, the Moluccas, New Guinea, Solomon's Islands, etc. Wallace first announced this ancient boundary, and it has been called ' Wallace's line.' He was led to infer its existence by the fact which he observed as he travelled about from island to island, that, while the faunas of these two regions are as wholes very different from each other, the faunas of the various land patches in each area have a wonderful similarity. Australia is a veritable museum of old and obsolete forms of both plants and animals. Its fauna and flora are made up prevailingly of forms such as have on the other continents long been superseded by more specialised species. No true mammals, excepting men and a few rats, lived in Australia when Englishmen first went there. The most powerful animals were the comparatively helpless marsupials. The explanation of these remarkable facts is probably this : The Australian continent, which formerly included New Guinea and other islands to the north, has not been connected with the other land masses for a very long period of time. The development upon the other continents of the more powerful mammals, especially of the ungulates and the carnivora, resulted in the extermination of the more helpless forms from most of the earth's surface. But Australia, protected by its isolation, has retained to this day its old-fashioned forms of life, neither land animals nor plants having been able to navigate the intervening straits. This supposition is strengthened by the fact that fossil remains of marsupials are to-day found scattered all over the world, while, with the exception of the American opossums, living marsupials are found only in Australia and its islands. There is to-day not a single survivor of these once-numerous races in either Europe, Asia, or Africa. Similar facts of distribution are furnished by the lemurs—those small, monkey-like animals with fox faces, which are sometimes called ' half-apes,' since they are supposed to be the link connecting the true apes with lower forms. Fossil lemurs are found in both America and Europe, but lemurs are now extinct in both continents. Those of America were probably exterminated by the carnivora, who are known to be very fond of monkey meat of all kinds. The European lemurs seem to have migrated southward into eastern Africa at a time when Madagascar formed a part of the mainland. ' There they have been isolated, and have developed in a fashion comparable to that which has occurred in the case of the Australian marsupials. Of fifty living species, thirty are confined to Madagascar, and the lemurs are there exceedingly numerous in individuals. Outside of Madagascar they only maintain a precarious footing in forests or on islands, and are usually few in number ' (10).

If the earth were peopled by migrations from Ararat, it would require a good deal of intellectual legerdemain to show why the sloths are confined to South America and the monotremes to Australia and its islands. The reindeer of northern Europe and Asia, and the elk and caribou of Arctic America, are so much alike they must have descended from a common ancestry, and been developed into distinct species since the separation of North America and Eurasia. The same thing is probably also true of the puma and jaguar, who inhabit the middle latitudes of the New World, and the lion, tiger, and leopard, occupying like latitudes of the Old World. They all belong to the cat family, and represent divergences from a common feline type of structure. The camel does not exist normally outside of northern Africa and central and western Asia. And when the camel-like llama of South America first became known to zoologists, it was a problem how this creature could have become separated so far from the apparent origin of the camel family. But since then fossil camels have been found all over both North and South America. And it has even been suspected that perhaps America was the original home of the camel, and that, like the horse, the camel migrated to the eastern hemisphere at a time when the eastern and western land masses were connected. The foxes, hares, and other mammals of the upper Alps, also many Alpine plants, are like those of the Arctic regions. The most probable explanation of these resemblances is that these Alpine species climbed up into these inhospitable altitudes, and were left stranded here on this island of cold, when their relatives, on the return of warmth at the close of the glacial period, retreated back to the ice-bound fastnesses around the pole. It is for a similar reason, probably, that the flora of the upper White Mountains resembles that of Labrador.

7. One of the strongest pieces of evidence bearing on evolution that is furnished by any department of knowledge is that furnished by geology. It is the evidence of the rocks. Geology is, among other things, a history of the earth. This history has been written by the earth itself on laminæ of stone. It is from these records that we learn incontestably the order in which the forms of life have made their appearance on the earth.

Three-fourths of the surface of the earth is sea. Over the surface of the remaining fourth, excepting in mountainous places, is a layer of soil, varying from a few feet to a few hundred feet in depth. Beneath this coverlet of soil, extending as far as man has penetrated into the earth, is rock. Excepting in regions overflowed by lava poured out from beneath, or along the backbones of continents where the surface rocks have been upheaved into folds and carried away by denudation, the rocks immediately beneath the soil, to a thickness often of thousands of feet, are in the form of layers, or sheets, arranged one above another. These rocks are called sedimentary rocks, as distinguished from the unlaminated rocks of the interior. They have been formed at the bottom of the sea, and have, hence, all been formed since the condensation of the oceans. They have been formed out of the detritus of continents brought down by the rivers and the accumulated remains of animal and vegetal forms which have slowly settled down through the waters. They are the successive cemeteries of the dead past. Such rocks are now forming over the floors of all oceans—forming just as they have formed throughout the long eons of geological history. Along the axes of ancient mountains and in deep-cut canyons the rock layers are exposed to a thickness of thousands of feet, in some cases thirty or forty thousand feet. Here they lie, piled up, one on top of another, the great, broad pages upon which are written the long, dark story of our planet. It is the mightiest and most everlasting of all annals —the autobiography of a world. It is possible, by studying these rock records, to know not only the kind of life that lived in each age, but a good deal regarding the conditions in which that life lived and passed away. Just as the naturalist is able, from a single bone of an unknown animal, to reconstruct the entire animal and to infer something of its surroundings and habits of life, and as the archeologist, by going back to the graves of deceased races and digging up the dust upon which these races wrought, is able to tell much of their history and characteristics, so the geologist, by studying the bones of those more distant civilisations, the civilisations sandwiched among the fossiliferous rocks, is able to know, not only just the kind of life that lived in each age, but, by comparing the species of successive strata, can construct with astonishing fulness the genealogical outline of the entire life process. The succession of life forms as they appear in the rocks, with a sketch of their probable genealogy, is traced elsewhere in this chapter. It is only necessary to say here that the order in which the forms of life appear in the sedimentary strata is that of a gradually increasing complexity. The invertebrates appear first; then the fishes, the lowest of the vertebrates; after these come the amphibians; following these the reptiles; and finally the birds and mammals.

8. There is another reason for a belief in evolution furnished by geology, but of a somewhat different kind from that just stated. It consists in the fact that there are found in the rocks series or grades of structures, which fit with amazing accuracy on to the structures of existing species. Now, this is precisely what, according to the evolutional hypothesis, is to be expected. For, if evolution is true, existing species represent the tops of things. They are the existing and visible parts of processes which extend indefinitely back into the past, and whose deceased stages may reasonably be expected to be found fossil in the earth. Considering the youth and inexperience of paleontology and the torn and incoherent character of the record, it is surprising that anatomists have been able to accomplish what they have accomplished. In many cases — notably,

those of man, the snail, the crocodile, and the horse—antecedent forms of structure have been found in almost unbroken gradations leading back to types differing immensely from their existing representatives. Bones and fossils of men have been found buried beneath the alluvium of rivers, under old lava-beds, and in caves, crusted over by the deposits of percolating waters. Many such fossils are found in quaternary rocks, along with the bones of animals still living and some extinct. Some of these remains indicate unmistakable affinities with the ape. The most celebrated of these discoveries is the fossil of an erect ape-man (*Pithecanthropus erectus*), found by a Dutch Governor on the island of Java in 1894. This fossil, in the shape and size of the head and in its general structure, strikes about as near as could be the middle between man and ape. That it is the fossil of an ambiguous form is indicated by the fact that, when it was examined by a company of twelve specialists at Berlin soon after its discovery, three of them declared it to be the remains of an individual belonging to a low variety of man; three others thought it was a large anthropoid; while the other six held that it was neither man nor anthropoid, but a genuine connecting link between them. It is discussed at length by Haeckel in 'The Last Link,' a paper read before the International Congress of Zoology, at Cambridge, in 1898. 'It is,' says the veteran biologist, 'the much-sought "missing link" supposed to be wanting in the chain of primates which stretches unbroken from the lowest catarhine to the most highly developed man.' Associated with this fossil ape-man were the fossils of the elephant, hyena, and hippopotamus, none of which any longer exist in that part of the world, also the fossil remains of two orders of animals now extinct. The genealogy of the crocodile has been traced by Huxley, through all intermediate stages, back to the giant reptiles of the early Tertiary.* And the pedigree of the horse has been even more completely worked out by the indefatigable Marsh. In the museum of Yale University may be seen the fossil history of this splendid ungulate, from the time it was a clumsy little quadruped only 14 inches high, and with four or five toes on each foot, down to existing horses. The earliest known ancestor of the horse, the eohippus, lived at the beginning of the Eocene epoch. It had five toes, almost equal, on each front foot (four toes behind), and was about the size of a fox. The orohippus, which lived a little later, had four toes on each front-foot, and three behind. The mesohippus, found in the Miocene, had three toes and one rudimentary toe on each front-foot, and three toes behind. It was about the size of a sheep. The miohippus, which is found later, had three toes on each of its four feet, with the middle toe on each foot larger than the other two. The pliohippus, living in the Pliocene epoch, had one principal toe on each foot, and two secondary toes, the two secondary toes not reaching to the ground. It was about the size of a

* See table of geological ages, p. 79.

donkey. Existing horses have one toe on each
foot—the digit corresponding to the big middle
finger—and the ruins of two others in the form of
splints on the back of each ankle.   In the embryo
of the horse these splints are segmented, each of
them, into three phalanges. Fossil remains representing all stages in the development of the horse
have been found in the regions about the upper
waters of the Missouri River.

It is an important fact that the types of structure forming any series grow more and more
generalised as the distance from the present
increases, and that different lines of development,
when traced back into the past, often converge in
types which combine the main characters of
various existing groups. The horses, rhinoceroses,
and tapirs, great as are the differences among
them now, can be traced back step by step through
fossil forms, their differences gradually becoming
less marked, until 'the lines ultimately blend
together, if not in one common ancestor, at all
events into forms so closely alike in all essentials
that no reasonable doubt can be held as to their
common origin.' 'The four chief orders of the higher
mammals—the primates, ungulates, carnivora, and
rodents—seem to be separated by profound gulfs,
when we confine our attention to the representatives of to-day. But these gulfs are completely
closed, and the sharp distinctions of the four orders
are entirely lost, when we go back and compare
their extinct predecessors of the Cenozoic period,
who lived at least three million years ago.   There

we find the great sub-class of the placentals, which to-day comprises more than two thousand five hundred species, represented by only a small number of insignificant pro-placentals, in which the characters of the four divergent orders are so intermingled and toned down that we cannot in reason do other than consider them as the precursors of those features. The oldest primates, the oldest ungulates, the oldest carnivora, and the oldest rodents, all have the same skeletal structure and the same typical dentition (forty-four teeth) as these pro-placentals; all are characterised by the small and imperfect structure of the brain, especially of the cortex, its chief part, and all have short legs and five-toed, flat-soled (plantigrade) feet. In many cases among these oldest placentals it was at first very difficult to say whether they should be classed with the primates, ungulates, carnivora, or rodents, so very closely and confusedly do these four groups, which diverge so widely afterwards, approach each other at that time. Their common origin from a single ancestral group follows incontestably ' (5).

9. Man is the most powerful and influential of animals. He rules the world—rules it with a sovereignty more despotic and extensive than that hitherto exercised by any other animal. Many races of beings are, and have been for centuries, completely dominated by him. These races, during their long subjection, have been changed and transformed by man in a wonderful manner through his control of their power to breed. All

domestic animals have come from wild animals; they have been derived by a process of selective evolution conducted by man himself. By continually choosing as the progenitors of each generation those with qualities best suited to his whims and purposes, man has evolved races as different from each other in appearance and structure, and as different from the original species, as many groups which, in the wild state, constitute distinct species; indeed, man has in some cases created entirely new species, both of plants and animals—species that breed true and are what biologists call 'good'—by his own selections.

There are something over 150 different varieties of the domestic pigeon. Some of these varieties—as many as a dozen, Mr. Darwin thinks—differ from each other sufficiently to be reckoned, if they are considered solely with reference to their structures, as entirely distinct species. The carrier, for instance, the giant of the pigeons, measures 17 inches from bill-tip to the end of its tail, and has a beak $1\frac{3}{4}$ inches long. Around each eye is a large dahlia-like wattle, and another large wattle is on the beak, giving the beak the appearance of having been thrust through the kernel of a walnut. The tumbler is small, squatty, and almost beakless. It has the preposterous habit of rising high in the air and then tumbling heels over head. The roller, one of the many varieties of the tumbler, descends to the ground in a series of back somersaults, executed so rapidly that it looks like a falling ball. The runt is large, weighing sometimes as much as the carrier. The fantail has thirty or forty feathers in its tail, while all other varieties have only twelve or fourteen, the normal number for birds. The trumpeter, so named on account of its peculiar coo, has an umbrella-like hood of feathers covering its head and face, and its feet are so heavily feathered that they look like little wings. In the correct specimens of this variety the feathers have to be clipped from the face before the birds can see to feed themselves. The pouter has the absurd habit of inflating its gullet to a prodigious size, and the Jacobin wears a gigantic ruff. The homing pigeon has such a strong attachment for its cote that it will travel hundreds of miles, sometimes as many as 1,400 miles, in order to reach the home from which it has been separated. But it is not simply in their colour, size, habits, and plumage, that pigeons vary. There are corresponding differences in their structures, in the number of their ribs and vertebræ, in the shape and size of the skull, in the bones of the face, in the development of the breast-bone, and in the length of the neck, legs, and bill. Pigeons also differ in the shape and size of their eggs, and in their dispositions and voice. ' There is,' says Huxley in summing up his discussion of the great variety in these birds, ' hardly a particular of either internal econony or external shape which has not by selective breeding been perpetuated and become the foundation of a new race ' (11).

All of the 150 different varieties of domestic

pigeons have been evolved by human selection during the past three or four thousand years from the blue rock-doves which to-day inhabit the sea-coast countries of Europe.

What is true of pigeons is also true largely of most of the other races associated with man—of cats, cattle, horses, sheep, swine, goats, fowls, and the like. All varieties of the domestic chicken — the clumsy Cochin with its feather-duster legs, the tall and stately Spanish, the great-crested Minorca, the Dorking with its matchless comb and wattle, the almost combless Polish, the blue Andalusian, the gigantic Brahma, the tiny Bantam, the Wyandottes in all colours (black, white, buff, silver, and golden), the magnificent Plymouth Rocks, and the exceedingly pugnacious Game-cock—these and dozens of other varieties, all flightless, have come from the jungle-bird whose morning clarion still greets Aurora from the wilds of distant India. The dog is a civilised wolf, and the wild-boar is the progenitor of the oleaginous swine. The Merino and South Down breeds of sheep have come from the same stock in the last century and a half. In 1790 a lamb was born on the farm of Seth Wright in Massachusetts. It had a long body and short, bowed legs. It was noticed that this lamb could not follow the others over the fences. The owner thought it would be a good thing if all his sheep were like it. So he selected it to breed from. Some of its offspring were like it, and some were like the ordinary sheep. By continual selection of those with long bodies and short legs the ancon breed of sheep was finally produced. In 1770 in a herd of Paraguay cattle a hornless male calf appeared, and from this individual in a similar way came the stock of Muleys. The occasional appearance of horned calves and lambs among the offspring of hornless breeds of cattle and sheep are examples of atavism indicating the presence of a vestigial tendency to breed true to their horned ancestors. The Hereford cattle originated as a distinct variety about 1769 through the careful selections of a certain Englishman by the name of Tompkins. All domesticated quadrupeds, except the elephant, have come from wild species with erect ears, the ears acting as funnels to harvest the sound-waves. But there are few of them in which there is not one or more varieties with drooping ears—cats in China, horses in parts of Russia, sheep in Italy, cattle in India, and pigs, dogs, and rabbits in all long-civilised lands. We are so accustomed to seeing dogs and pigs with pendent ears that we are surprised to know there are varieties with erect ears. The goldfish is a carp, and in its native haunts in the waters of China it has the colour of the carp. The golden hue seen in the occupants of our aquaria has been given to this fish by the Chinese through the continual selection of certain kinds. The goldfish, almost as much as the pigeon, has been the sport of fanciers, and the strangest varieties have resulted. Some have outlandishly long fins, while others have no dorsal fin at all. Some are streaked and splotched with gold and scarlet;

others are pure albinos. One of the most monstrous varieties has a three-lobed tail-fin, and its eye-balls, without sockets, are on the outside of its head.   All of our common barnyard fowls—turkeys, ducks, geese, and chickens—are flight-less, but the varieties from which the domesticated forms have come all have functional wings, two of these varieties crossing continents in their annual migrations.

Not only animals, but plants also, many of them, have been greatly changed by man in his efforts to adapt them to his uses as food, orna-mentation, and the like.   On the seaside cliffs of Chili and Peru may still be found growing the wild-potato—the small, tough, bitter ancestor of the mammoth Burbank, Peerless, Early Rose, and the nearly two hundred other varieties of this matchless tuber found in the gardens of civilised man.   The cabbage, kale, cauliflower, and kohl-rabi are all modifications of the same wild species (*Brassica oleracea*), the cauliflower being the de-veloped flower, kohlrabi the stalk, and kale and cabbage the leaves.   The peach and the almond, Darwin thinks, have also come from a common ancestral drupe, the peach being the developed fruit, and the almond the seed.   There are nearly 900 different varieties of apples, varying in the most wonderful manner in size, colour, flavour, texture, and shape, but all of them probably derived from the little, sour, inedible Asiatic crab. The many times ' double ' roses of our gardens have come from the five-petalled wild-rose of the prairies. The cultivated varieties of viburnum and hydrangea have showy corymbs of infertile flowers only, but the wild forms from which the domestic varieties have been derived have only a single marginal row of showy infertile flowers surrounding a mass of inconspicuous fertile flowers. It has been due to their efforts to please men that bananas, pineapples, and oranges have got into the habit of neglecting to produce seeds. There are certain species of grapes that are seedless, also seedless sugar-cane, and a seedless apple has just been announced by horticulturists. The development of domesticated plants is only in its infancy, and it is probably impossible even for the most agile imagination to dream of the miracles the horticulturist is destined to work in the ages to come. There is every reason to believe that seedless varieties of all our common fruits will ultimately be produced, and that in size, flavour, nutrient constituents, and appearance, they will be developed into forms utterly different from existing varieties. Just within the last few years the U.S. Department of Agriculture has developed a cotton-plant immune to the bacterial diseases of the soil, which had completely driven the cotton-raising industry out of large districts of the South. The cultivation of many of the cereals has gone on so long, and has proceeded so far, that their origin is lost in antiquity.

Whether or not it is possible for new varieties and species to be evolved is a question, therefore, which does not need to depend for reply wholly upon theory. It is *known* to have taken place; and the process by which the different varieties of domestic animals and plants have been evolved—domestic selection—is not different in principle from the process of natural selection, the chief operation by which life in general, both plant and animal, is assumed to have been evolved.

10. There are other reasons for a belief in organic evolution, but the last one I shall mention is the fact that the theory of organic evolution harmonises with the known tendencies of the universe as a whole. The organic kingdoms of the earth—animals and plants—are as truly parts of the terrestrial globe as the inorganic kingdom is; and as such they share in, and are actuated by, the same great tendency or instinct as that which actuates the whole. Nine-tenths of the substance of all animals and plants is oxygen, hydrogen, carbon, and nitrogen—the very elements which make up the entire ocean and air, and enter largely into the composition of the continents. The human body, which has essentially the same chemical composition as the bodies of animals in general, is made up of four solids, five gases, and seven metals—in all, sixteen elements of the something like seventy which constitute the entire planet. ' In the past, man appeared to be a creature foreign to the earth, and placed upon it as a transitory inhabitant by some incomprehensible power. The more perfect insight of the present day sees man as a being whose development has taken place in accordance with

the same laws as those that have governed the development of the earth and its entire organisation—a being not put upon the earth accidentally by an arbitrary act, but produced in harmony with the earth's nature, and belonging to it as do the flowers and the fruits to the tree which bears them.' Animals are not outside of, nor distinct from, the universe, as one might suspect who has listened much to the recital of tradition so long accepted as science. They are more or less detached portions of the planet earth which move over its surfaces and through its fluids and multiply, but which in their phenomena obey the same laws of chemistry and physics as those in accordance with which the rest of the universe acts. Animals are moulds through which digressing matters from the soil, sea, and sky pass on rounds of eternal itineracy.

Now, the earth as a planet is in process of evolution. Not many things are more certain than this. The earth has come out of fire. It has *grown* to be what it is. Its mountains, valleys, plains, seas, shores, islands, lakes, rivers, and continents—these were not always here. They have been evolved. Not only the earth, but the entire family of spheres of which the earth is a member—the solar system—are all evolving. Mr. Spencer never did anything more profound than when he demonstrated in his 'Law and Cause of Progress' the universal migration of things from a condition of homogeneity toward a condition of greater and greater heterogeneity.

The whole universe, or as much of it as can be examined by terrestrial instruments, has probably evolved out of the same primordial matters. The organic part of the earth has evolved, therefore, and is destined to continue to evolve, because it is a part of a whole whose habit or ambition it is to evolve.

The evidence is overwhelming. The theory of organic evolution is sustained by a mass of facts not less authoritative and convincing than that which supports the Copernican theory of the worlds. Evolution is, in fact, a doctrine so apparent that it only needs to be honestly and intelligently looked into to be accepted unreservedly. It is, indeed, *more* than a *doctrine*. It is a *known fact*. It is a *necessary effect* of the *conditions known to exist* among the animals and plants of the earth. If beings *vary* among themselves generation after generation, if only the *fittest* of each generation *survive*, and if the survivors tend to *transmit* to their offspring the qualities of their superiority (and the animals and plants of the earth are known to do continually all of these things), then it follows *with mathematical certainty* that evolution is going on, and that it will continue to go on as long as these conditions continue. It is inevitable. It could not be otherwise. We would *know* that evolution were going on among organisms where these conditions existed, even though we had never observed it.

The boldest and most enthusiastic opponents of

evolution have always been those with the least information about it. But the evidence is accumulating so rapidly, and is being drawn up in such unanswerable array, that, if it is not already the case, it will not be many years before it will be an intellectual reproach for anyone to discredit, or to be known to have discredited, this splendid and inspiring revelation.

X. The Genealogy of Animals.

Life originated in the sea, and for an immense period of time after it commenced it was confined to the place of its origin. The civilisations of the earth were for many millions of years exclusively aquatic. It has, indeed, been estimated that the time required by the life process in getting out of the water—that is, that the time consumed in elaborating the first species of land animals—was much longer than the time which has elapsed since then. I presume that during a large part of this early period it would have seemed to one living at that time extremely doubtful whether there would ever be on the earth any other kinds of life than the aquatic. And if those who to-day weave the fashionable fabrics of human philosophy, and who know nothing about anything outside the thin edge of the present, had been back there, they would no doubt have declared confidently, as they looked upon the naked continents and the uninhabited air and the sea teeming with its peculiar faunas, that life upon solids or in gases, life anywhere, in fact, except in the sea, where it had always existed, and to which alone it was adapted, was absolutely, and would be forever, impossible; and that feathered fishes and fishes with the power to run and skip, and especially 'sharks' competent to walk on one end and jabber with the other, were unthinkable nonsense. Life originated in the sea for the same reason that the first of the series of so-called 'civilisations' which have appeared in human history sprang from the alluvium of the Euphrates and the Nile, because the conditions for bringing life into existence were here the most favourable. The atmosphere was incompetent to perform such a task as the inventing of *protoplasm*, and there was no land above the oceans.

The first forms of life were one-celled—simple, jelly-like dots of almost homogeneous plasm—the *protozoa*. These primitive organisms were the common grandparents of all beings. From them evolved, through infinite travail and suffering, all of the orders, families, species, and varieties of animals that to-day live on the earth, and all those that have in the past lived and passed away. By the multiplication and specialisation of cells, and the formation of cell aggregates, the sponges, celenterates, and flat worms were developed from the protozoa.* The connecting links between the one-celled and the many-celled animals consist of a series of colonial forms of increasing size and complexity, some of which may be found in every roadside ditch and pool, while

* See 'Genealogy of Animals,' p. 331.

others are extinct. The development of these many-celled organisms (metazoa) from one-celled organisms was a perfectly natural process, a process which takes place in the initial evolutions of every embryo. There is no more mystery about it than there is about any other act of association. All association is simply a matter of 'business.' Many-celled organisms are colonies, or societies, of more or less closely co-operating one-celled organisms, and they have come into existence in obedience to the same laws of economy and advantage as have those more modern societies of metazoa known as nations, communities, and states, the organised bodies of men, ants, and millionaires.

The sponges are the lowest of the many-celled animals. They consist of irregular masses of loosely associated cells, hopelessly anchored to the sea-floor. They represent the social instinct in embryo. The cells are but slightly specialised, and each cell leads a more or less independent existence. The sponge stands at about that stage of social integration and intelligence represented by those stupendous porifera which cover continents and constitute the 'social organisms' of the civilised world. The nutritive system of sponges consists of countless pores opening from the surface into a common canal within, through which ever-waving cilia urge the alimental waters. In the celenterates the cells arrange themselves in the form of a cup with one large opening into and from the vase-like stomach. The unsegmented

worms are flat and sac-like, with bilateral symmetry and the power to move about, but not
tubular, as are the true worms.   They are blood-
less, like the celenterates and sponges.

From the flat worms developed the annelid
worms, animals perforated by a food canal and
possessing a body cavity filled with blood surrounding this canal.   The body cavity is the space
between the walls of the body and the alimentary
canal, the cavity which in the higher animals
contains the heart, liver, lungs, kidneys, etc.   The
worms and all animals above them have this
cavity.   The worms and all animals above them
also have, as an inheritance from the flat worms,
bodies with bilateral symmetry—that is, bodies
with two halves similar.   This peculiarity was
probably acquired by the flat worms, and so
fastened upon all subsequently evolved species, as
a result of pure carelessness.   It probably arose
out of the habit of using continually, or over and
over again, the same parts of the body as fore and
aft.   It has been facetiously said that if it had not
been for this habit, so inadvertently acquired by
these humble beings so long, long ago, we would
not to-day be able to tell our right hand from our
left.   In the worm is found the beginning of
that wonderful organ of co-ordination, the brain.
The brain is a modification of the skin.   It may
weaken our regard for this imperial organ to know
that it is, in its morphology, akin to nails and
corns.   But it will certainly add to our admiration
for the infinite labours of evolution to remember

that the magnificent thinking apparatus of modern philosophers was originally a small sensitive plate developed down in the sea a hundred million years ago on the dorsal wall of the mouths of primeval worms.

From the worms developed all of the highest four phyla of the animal kingdom—the echinoderms, the mollusks, the arthropods, and the chordate animals, the last of which were the progenitors of the illustrious vertebrates. The lowest of the mollusks are the snails, and from these humble tenants of our ponds and shores sprang the headless bivalves and the giant jawed cuttles. The mollusks were for a long time after their development the mailed monarchs of the sea, and shared with the worms the dominion of the primordial waters. But after the development of the more active arthropods, especially the crustaceans, the less agile worms and mollusks rapidly declined. Existing worms and mollusks are remnants of once powerful and populous races.

From the worms also developed the arthropods, the water-breathing crustaceans and the air-breathing spiders and insects. The crustaceans came early, away back in the gray of the Silurian period, just about the time North America was born. North America lay, a naked, V-shaped infant, in the regions of Labrador and Canada. The crustaceans rapidly superseded the mollusks as rulers of the sea, attaining, in extreme species, a length of four or five feet. The spiders and

insects came into existence toward the latter part
of the Silurian period,* probably contemporaneous,
or nearly so, with the appearance of land vegeta-
tion. The spiders and insects were the aborigines
of the land and air. They are the only races of
living beings, except the original inhabitants of
the sea, who ever invaded and settled an unoccupied world. The earliest land fossils so far found
are the fossils of scorpions. But the existence of
a *sting* among the structural possessions of these
animals indicates that there were already others
who contended with them for supremacy in the
new world. The first insects were the masticating
insects, insects such as cockroaches, crickets, grass-
hoppers, dragon-flies, and beetles. They are found
abundantly in the Devonian and Carboniferous
rocks. The licking insects (bees) and the pricking
insects (flies and bugs) appeared first in the

---

* The following are the divisions and subdivisions of
geological history :

5. Cenozoic Era (Tertiary) -	Pleistocene period. Pliocene „ Miocene „ Oligocene „ Eocene „
4. Mesozoic Era (Secondary) -	Cretaceous period. Jurassic „ Triassic „
3. Paleozoic Era (Primary) -	Permian period. Carboniferous period. Devonian „ Silurian „ Ordovician „ Cambrian „
2. Proterozoic Era - - -	Algonkian period.
1. Archeozoic Era.	

Mesozoic Era, and the sipping insects (butter-flies) in the Cenozoic. The flower-loving insects (the bees and butterflies) came into the world at the same time as did the flowers. The wings of insects may be modifications of the gills used by insect young in respiration during their aquatic existence. They are, hence, very different in origin from the wings of birds, which are the modified fore-legs of reptiles.

The most important class of animals arising out of the worms, on account of their distinguished offspring, were the hypothetical cord animals. The only existing species allied to these animals is the amphioxus, a strange, unpromising-looking creature, half worm and half fish, found in the beach sands of many seas. It has white blood and a tubular heart. It is without either head or limbs, and looks very much like a long semi-transparent leaf, tapering at both ends. But it has two unmistakable prophecies of the vertebrate anatomy: a cartilaginous rod, pointed at both ends, extending along the back, and above this, and parallel to it, a cord of nerve matter. These are the same positions occupied by the spinal column and spinal cord in all true vertebrates. That the amphioxus is a genuine relative of the ancestor of the vertebrates is also shown by the fact that these simple forms of column and cord possessed by amphioxus are precisely the forms assumed by the spinal column and spinal cord in the embryos of all vertebrates, including man.

From these quasi-vertebrates developed the fishes

—first (after the scaleless, limbless lampreys) the sharks with spiny scales and cartilaginous skeleton, and after these the lung fishes and the bony fishes, with flat, horny scales and skeletons of bone. From the beginning of the Devonian age, when fishes first came into prominence, till the rise of the great reptiles in the Triassic time, fishes were the dominant life of the sea. In the fishes first appeared jaws, a sympathetic nervous system, red blood, backbone, and the characteristic two pairs of limbs of vertebrates.

The lung fishes (Dipneusta), a small order of strange salamander-like creatures which live ingeniously on the borderland between the liquid and the land, may be looked upon as physiological, if not morphological, links between the fishes and the frogs. They combine the characters of both fishes and frogs, and zoologists have been tempted to make a separate class of them, and place them between the two classes to which they are related. They are like fishes in having scales, fins, permanent gills, and a fish-like shape and skeleton. They resemble frogs in having lungs, nostrils, an incipiently three-chambered heart, a pulmonary circulation, and frog-like skin glands. There are three genera with several species. One genus (Neoceratodus) is found in two or three small rivers of Queensland, Australia; another (Protopterus) lives in the Gambia and other rivers of Africa; and the third (Lepidosiren) inhabits the swamps of the Amazon region. They all breathe ordinarily by means of gills, like true fishes, but have the habit of coming frequently to the surface and inhaling air. The air-bladder acts as an incipient lung in supplementing respiration by gills. They all live in regions where a dry season regularly converts the watercourses into beds of sand and mud. During the season of drought these strange animals build for themselves a cocoon or nest of mud and leaves. This cocoon is lined with mucus, and provided with a lid through which air is admitted. Here they lie in this capsule throughout the hot southern summer, from August to December, breathing air by means of their lungs and living upon the stored-up fat of their tails, until the return of the wet season, when they again live in the rivers and breathe water in true piscatorial fashion. These capsules have often been carried to Europe, and opened 3,000 miles from their place of construction without harming the life within.

Here, in these eccentric denizens of the southern world, we find the beginnings of a grand transformation—a transformation in both structure and function, a transformation made necessary by the transition from life in the water to life in the air, a transformation which reaches its maturity in the higher air-breathing vertebrates, where the simple air-sac of the fish becomes a pair of lobed and elaborately sacculated lungs, performing almost exclusively the function of respiration, and the gills change into parts of the ears and lower jaw.

The air-bladder of ordinary fishes, which is used chiefly as a hydrostatic organ to enable the fish to rise and fall in the water, is probably the degenerated lung of the lung fishes.

From the lung fishes or allied forms developed the amphibians, the well-known fish quadrupeds of our bogs and brooks. The amphibians are genuine connectives—living links between the life of the sea and the life of the land. In early life they are fishes, with gills and two-chambered hearts. In later life they are air-breathing quadrupeds, with legs and lungs and three-chambered hearts. Here is evolution, plenty of it, and of the most tangible character. And it takes place right before the eyes. The transformation from the fish to the frog is, however, no more wonderful than the embryonic transformations of other vertebrates. It is simply more apparent, because it can be seen. The lungs of amphibians and the lower reptiles are simple sacks opening by a very short passage into the mouth. Some amphibians, as the axolotl of Mexican lakes, ordinarily retain their gills through life, but may be induced to develop lungs and adapt themselves to terrestrial life by being kept out of the water. Others, as the newts, which ordinarily develop lungs, may be compelled to retain their gills through life by being forced to remain uninterruptedly in the water. The black salamander, inhabiting droughty regions of the Alps, brings forth its young bearing lungs, and only a pair at a time. But if the young are prematurely removed from the body of the mother and placed in the water, they develop gills in the ordinary way. These are remarkable instances of elasticity in the presence of a varying environment.

In the amphibians the characteristic five-toed or five-fingered foot, which normally forms the extremities of the limbs of all vertebrates except fishes, is first met with. It was this pentadactyl peculiarity of the frog, inherited by men and women through the reptiles and mammals, that gave rise to the decimal system of numbers and other unhandy facts in human life. The decimal system arose out of the practice of early men performing their calculations on their fingers. This method of calculating is still used by primitive peoples all over the world. The sum of the digits of the two hands came, in the course of arithmetical evolution, to be used as a unit, and from this simple beginning grew up the complicated system of tens found among civilised peoples. It has all come about as a result of amphibian initiative. Our very arithmetics have been predetermined by the anatomical peculiarities of the frog's foot. If these unthinking foreordainers of human affairs had had four or six toes on each foot instead of five, man would no doubt have inherited them just as cheerfully as the number he did inherit, and the civilised world would in this case be to-day using in all of its mathematical activities a system of eights or twelves instead of a system of tens. A system of eights or twelves would be much superior in flexibility to the existing system; for eight is a cube, and its half and double are squares; and twelve can be divided by two, three, four, and six, while ten is divisible by two and five only.

How helpless human beings are—in fact, how helpless all beings are! How hopelessly dependent we are upon the past, and how impossible it is to be really original! What the future will be depends upon what the present is, for the future will grow out of, and inherit, the present. What the present is depends upon what the past was, for the present has grown out of, and inherited, the past. And what the past was depends upon a remoter past from which it evolved, and so on. There is no end anywhere of dependence, either forward or backward. Every fact, from an idea to a sun, is *a contingent link in an eternal chain.*

From the amphibians (probably from extinct forms, not from living) there arose the highest three classes of vertebrates—the true reptiles, the birds, and the mammals—all of whom have lungs and breathe air from the beginning to the end of their days. Gills, as organs of breathing, disappear forever, being changed, as has been said, into parts of the organs of mastication and hearing. In the reptiles first appear those organs which in the highest races overflow on occasions of tenderness and grief, the tear glands. These organs are, however, in our cold-blooded antecedents, organs of ocular lubrication rather than of weeping. There are but four small orders of existing reptiles —snakes, turtles, lizards, and crocodilians. These are the pygmean descendants of a mighty line, the last of a dynasty which during the greater part of the Mesozoic ages was represented by the most immense and powerful monsters that have ever lived upon the earth. Mesozoic civilisation was pre-eminently saurian. Reptiles were supreme everywhere—on sea and land and in the air. Their rulership of the world was not so bloody and masterful as man's, but quite as remorseless. Imagine an aristocracy made up of pterosaurs (flying reptiles), with teeth, and measuring 20 feet between wing-tips; great plesiosaurs (serpent reptiles) and ichthyosaurs (fish reptiles), enormous bandits of the seas; and dinosaurs and atlantosaurs, giant land lizards, 30 feet high and from 50 to 100 feet in length. A government of demagogs is bad enough, as king-ridden mankind well know, but dragons would be worse, if possible. The atlantosaurs were the largest animals that have ever walked upon the earth. They were huge plant-eaters inhabiting North America. It has been surmised that one of these behemoths 'may have consumed a whole tree for breakfast.' It was the mighty saurians of the Mesozoic time who brought into everlasting subordination the piscatorial civilisation of the Devonian and carboniferous ages.

Toward the latter part of the Reptilian Age, and somewhere along about the time of the appearance of hard-wood forests, came the birds, those beautiful and emotional beings who, in spite of human destructiveness, continue to fill our groves and gardens with the miracles of beauty and song. The bird is a 'glorified reptile.' How the 'slow, cold-blooded, scaly saurian ever became transformed into the quick, hot-blooded, feathered bird, the joy of creation,' is a considerable mystery, yet we know no reason for believing that the transformation did not take place. Although in their external appearance and mode of life birds and reptiles differ so widely from each other, yet, in their internal structure and embryology, they are so much alike that one of the brightest anatomists that has ever lived (Huxley) united them both into a single class under the name Sauropsida. It might naturally be supposed that the birds are descendants of the flying reptiles, the pterosaurs. But this may not be true. The pterosaurs were structurally much further removed from the birds than were certain extinct terrestrial reptiles. The fact that birds and pterosaurs both had wings has really nothing to do with the case. For the wings of reptiles, we almost know, were not homologous with the wings of birds. The bird's wing is a feathered fore-leg; the wing of the reptile was an expanded skin stretching from the much-elongated last finger backwards to the hind-leg and tail. Wings, it may be remarked in passing, have had at least four different and distinct beginnings in the animal kingdom, represented by the bats, the birds, the reptiles, and the insects. This does not include the parachutes of the so-called flying squirrels, lemurs, lizards, phalangers, and fishes.

The first birds had teeth and vertebrated tails. The archeopteryx, which is the earliest toothed bird whose remains have yet been found, was about the size of a crow. It had thirty-two teeth and twenty caudal vertebræ. Two specimens of it have been found in the Jurassic slates of Bavaria. One of these fossils is in the British Museum, and the other in the Museum of Berlin. Other toothed birds have been found fossil by Dr. Mudge in the cretaceous chalk of North America. These last had short, fan tails like existing birds.

From the toothed birds developed the beaked birds—the keel-breasted birds (the group to which most existing birds belong) and the birds with unkeeled breasts, *i.e.*, the ostrich-like birds. The ostrich-like birds are runners. They have rudimentary wings, and the keel of the breast-bone, which in the keel-breasted birds acts as a stay for the attachment of the wing muscles, is lacking. The ostrich-like birds are probably degenerate flyers, the flying apparatus having become obsolete through disuse. The feathers of birds are generally supposed to be the modified scales of reptiles.

The most brilliant offspring of the reptiles were the mammals, animals capable of a wider distribution over the face of the earth than the cold-blooded reptiles, on account of their hair and their warm blood. Cold-blooded animals of great size are able to inhabit but a small zone of the existing earth's surface—the torrid belt. They cannot house themselves during the seasons of cold, as men can; nor escape to the tropics on the wings of the wind, as do the birds ; nor bury themselves in subaqueous mud, as do the frogs, snakes, and crustaceans. During the Mesozoic period, when cold - blooded reptiles of gigantic size flourished over a wide area of the earth's surface, the planet was far warmer than now. Animals, therefore, like the mammals (or birds), capable of maintaining a fixed temperature regardless of the thermal fluctuations of the surrounding media, are the only animals of large size and power capable of uninterrupted existence over the greater part of the surface of the existing earth. The pre-eminent life of the Cenozoic time was mammalian. But the decline and fall of the saurian power was not wholly due to the rise of the more dynamic mammals. It was in part due, no doubt, to adverse conditions of climate, and also to the fact that mammals and birds guard their eggs, and saurians do not.

The lowest of the mammals are the monotremes, animals which blend in a marvellous manner the characteristics of birds, reptiles, and mammals. Only two families of these old-fashioned creatures are left, the echidna and the duck-bill (ornitho-rhynchus), both of them found on or near that museum of biological antiquities, Australia. They are covered with hair and suckle their young like other mammals, but they have only the rudiments of milk glands, and they lay eggs with large yolks from a cloaca, like the reptiles and birds. The duck-bill hides its eggs in the ground, but the echidna hatches its eggs in a small external brooding pouch, periodically developed for this purpose. The young of the monotremes feed on the oily perspiration which exudes from the body of the mother. The monotremes first appear in the fossiliferous rocks of the Triassic Age.

From the monotreme-like mammals developed the marsupial mammals, animals possessing a purse-like pouch on the after part of the abdomen, in which they carry their young. The young of marsupials are born in an extremely immature state, and are carried in this pouch in order to complete their development. The young of the kangaroo, an animal as large as a man, are only about an inch in length when they arc born. They are carried for nine months after their birth in the marsupium of the mother, firmly attached to the maternal nipple. The marsupials came into existence during the Jurassic Age, and during the next age, the Cretaceous, they arose to considerable power. During this latter age they were found on every continent. But they have been almost exterminated by their more powerful descendants.

From the marsupials developed the placental mammals, animals so called because their young are developed within the parental body in association with a peculiar nourishing organ called the placenta. From the herbivorous marsupials developed the almost toothless edentates, the rodents, or gnawing animals, the sirenians, the cetaceans, and the hoofed animals, or ungulates. The sirenians are fish-like animals with two flippers, and are often called sea-cows. They resemble whales in many respects, and are sometimes classed with them. They are plant-eaters exclusively, and are found grazing along the bottoms of tropical estuaries and rivers. They have tiny eyes, teeth fitted for grinding (not spike-like as in the whales), and a strong affection for their young, the mother, when pursued, often carrying her little one under her flippers. An immense sirenian, known as Steller's manatee, was discovered on the Behring Islands, along the Kamschatka coast, in 1741. Twenty-seven years afterwards not one of them was left, all having been murdered by the Russian sailors. The sirenians are probably degenerate forms of land quadrupeds, having lost their hind-limbs and developed the fish-like shape in adapting themselves to aquatic conditions. They appear first in the Eocene Age.

Among the most interesting derivatives of the herbivorous marsupials, because the most aberrant, are the whales. They are true mammals—have warm blood, breathe the air with lungs, and suckle their young like other mammals. But, like the sirenians, they live in the surface of the waters, and have flippers and a fish-like tail and form. They differ from the sirenians, however, in being carnivorous, in having inguinal instead of pectoral milk glands, and in being structurally less like quadrupeds. They probably degenerated from land quadrupeds during the Jurassic period, and, owing to their longer residence in the waters, have become further removed from the quadrupedal type than the sirenians. Whales have two limbs, the hind-limbs having disappeared as a result of the pre-eminent development of the tail. The tails of whales and sirenians are flattened horizontally, not vertically, as in fishes.

Out of generalised forms of hoofed animals now extinct developed the odd-toed and even-toed races of existing ungulates. The original ungulates had five hoofs on each foot, and were highly generalised in their structure. From these original five-toed forms have arisen the variously hoofed and variously structured tribes of existing ungulates: the five-toed elephant, the four-toed tapir and hippopotamus, the three-toed rhinoceros, the two-toed camel, sheep, swine, deer, antelope, giraffe, and ox, and the one-toed horse and zebra.

The carnivorous branch of the placental animals came from the carnivorous branch of the marsupials. From early forms of carnivorous placentals developed the ape-like lemurs and those generalised forms of rapacious animals from which arose the insect-eaters, the bats, and the true carnivora. The seals represent a by-development from the main line of the carnivora, a third defection, and a comparatively recent one, from land faunas. Seals live at the meeting of the land and the waters rather than in or on the waters, as do the cetaceans and sirenians. They have retained their fur and their four limbs, but have almost lost their power of land locomotion by the conversion of their feet into flippers. The two front-limbs of seals are the only ones used as ordinary limbs are used. The hind-limbs in most seals stretch permanently out behind, the webbed digits spreading out fan-shaped on either side of the stumpy tail, and constituting a rowing apparatus functionally homologous with the tail of fishes and whales. According to Jordan, the fur seals and the hair seals are descended from different families of land carnivora, the former probably from the bears, and the latter from the cats.

The lemurs are of especial interest to human beings, because in them are found the first startling approximation in looks and structure to the 'human form divine.' The lemurs are monkey-like creatures living in trees, but differ enough from true monkeys to be often placed in an order by themselves. Their milk glands are abdominal instead of pectoral, as in the monkeys, and the second digit of each hand and foot ends in a claw. The most of them live in Madagascar. They are generally nocturnal in their habits, although some species are diurnal. They appear first in the Eocene rocks, and Haeckel thinks they may have developed from opossum-like marsupials in the late Cretaceous or early Eocene Age.

From lemurs or from some other similar sort of semi-apes developed the true apes—the flat-nosed (platyrhine) apes of the New World and the narrow-nosed (catarhine) apes of the Old World. There is considerable difference between the New World apes and those of the Old World. The differences between the two classes is, in fact, so striking that they are thought by some to have developed independently of each other from distinct species of semi-apes. The apes of the New World have flat noses, and the nostrils are far apart and open in front of the nose, never below. The Old World apes have narrow noses, the nostrils being close together and opening downwards as in man. The tail of (nearly) all New World apes is prehensile, being used regularly as a fifth limb, while among Old World apes the tail is never so used. The Old World apes all have the same number and kinds of teeth as man has, while the New World apes (excepting the Brazilian marmosets) have an additional premolar in each half-jaw, making thirty-six in all. The catarhine apes are, therefore, structurally much nearer to man than their platyrhine cousins. All tailed apes probably sprang originally from a single stirp of semi-apes, and spread over the earth at a time when the eastern and western land masses of the southern hemisphere were connected with each other. The earliest remains of apes appear in the Miocene Age.

From the Old World tailed apes were developed the tailless, man-like, or anthropoid apes—the gorillas and chimpanzees of Africa, and the orangs and gibbons of Asia and the East Indies. The anthropoids arose from the tailed apes by the loss of the tail, the thinning of the hairy covering, the enlargement of the fore-brain, and by structural adaptations to a more nearly vertical position. No remains of anthropoids are found earlier than the Pliocene Age.

The man-like apes are the nearest living relatives of the human races. It is not probable that man has been derived directly from any of the existing races of man-like apes. For no one of them in all particulars of its structure stands closer to him than the rest. The orang approaches closest to man in the formation of the brain, the chimpanzee in the shape of the spine and in certain characteristics of the skull, the gorilla in the development of the feet and in size, and the gibbon in the formation of the throat and teeth. The earliest human races probably sprang from man-like races of apes now extinct, who lived in southern Asia or in Africa during the Pliocene Age (possibly as early as the Miocene), and who combined in their structures the various man-like characters possessed by existing anthropoids.

The earliest races of men were speechless—the ape-like 'Alali'—beings, living wholly upon the ground and walking upon their hind-limbs, but without more than the mere rudiments of language. The vertical position led to a much greater development of the posterior parts, especially of the muscles of the back and the calves of the leg. The great toe, which in the ape is opposable, lost its opposability, or all except traces of it, after the abandonment of arboreal life. It must have been a sight fit to stir the soul of the most leathern, these children of the night, with low brows, stooping gait, and ape-like faces, armed with rude clubs, clothed in natural hair, and wandering about in droves without law, fire, or understanding, hiding in thickets and in the holes of the earth, feeding on roots and fruits, and contending doubtfully with the species around them for food and existence.

From the ' Alali '—the speechless ape-men—we may imagine the true men to have evolved—talking men, men with erect posture and mature brain and larynx, the woolly-haired ulotrichi and the straight-haired lissotrichi. There are four existing species of woolly-haired men : the Papuans of New Guinea and Melanesia, and the Hottentots, Caffres, and Negroes of southern, equatorial, and north central Africa respectively. They all have long heads, slanting teeth, very dark skin, and black, bushy hair, each individual hair in cross-section being flat or oval in shape. In the straight-haired races the skin is much fairer than in the woolly-haired races, being seldom darker than brown, and each individual hair in cross-section is round like the cross-section of a cylinder. The principal species of straight-haired men are the sea-roving Malays of the East Indies and the Pacific, the round-faced Mongols of eastern and northern Asia, the aboriginal Americans of the western hemisphere, and the incomparable Aryans, including the ancient Greeks and Romans and the modern peoples of India, Persia, and Europe.

Man is to-day the pre-eminent animal of the planet. The successive ascendancies of the Worm, the Mollusk, the Crustacean, the Fish, the Reptile, and the Mammal, are followed triumphantly by the ascendancy of the Children of the Ape.

A large part of the life of the earth has remained steadfastly where it was cradled, beneath the waves. But more restless portions have left the sea and crept forth upon the land, or swarmed into the air. One migration, the most numerous, is represented by the insects. Another, the most enterprising, was the amphibian. After ages of evolution the amphibian branch divided. One branch acquired wings and sailed off into the air. The other divided and subdivided. One of these subdivisions entered the forests, climbed and clambered among the trees, acquired perpendicularity and hands, descended and walked upon the soil, invented agriculture, built cities and states, and imagined itself immortal. Human society is but the van—the hither terminus—of an evolutional process which had its beginning away back in the protoplasm of primeval waters. There is not a form that creeps beneath the sea but can claim kinship with the eagle. The philosopher is the remote posterity of the meek and lowly amœba.

XI. Conclusion.

The resemblances, homologies, and metamorphoses existing everywhere among animal forms are, therefore, evidence of the most logical consanguinities. It is all so perfectly plain. The structures of organic beings have come about as a result of the action and reaction of environment upon these structures. Every being—and not only every being, but every species, the whole organic world—has come to be what it is as a result of the incessant hammerings of its surroundings, the hammerings not only of the present, but of the long-stretching past. By surroundings is meant, of course, the rest of the universe. Those animals belonging to the same stock resemble each other because they have been subjected to the same experiences, the same series of selections. They have lain on the same great anvil, and felt the down-comings of the same sledge. The similarities among animal forms in general indicate relationships, just as the similarities among the races of men indicate racial consanguinities. All men belong to the human species because they are all fundamentally alike. But there are differences in the character of the hair, in the colour of the skin, in the conformation of the skull, and in the structure of the language, among the different varieties of the species, indicating striking variety in relationship and origin. An eminent biologist has said that if Negroes and Caucasians were snails they would be classed as entirely distinct species of animals. Whether, as is thought by some, the woolly-haired races are the descendants of the African anthropoids, and the straight-haired varieties are the posterity of the orangs and gibbons, we may never know positively. But we do know that these two great branches of mankind must have different genealogies, extending to a remote antiquity, and that the varieties belonging to each great group sustain to each other the relations of a common kinship. English-

men look like each other, act like each other, and
speak the same language. So do Frenchmen and
Swedes and Chinese. Every people is peculiar.
This is not the result of accident or agreement,
but the result of law. Mongolians do not all have
short heads, yellow faces, slanting eyes, and prominent malars because they have agreed to have
them, but as a result of a common pedigree.
Similarity of structure implies commonalty of
origin, and commonalty of origin means consanguinity.

And this is true whether you contemplate the
featural resemblances of brothers and sisters of
the same human parent, or those more fundamental characteristics which distinguish species,
orders, and sub-kingdoms. All animals are composed of protoplasm, which is a compound of
clay, because all animals are descended from the
same first parents, protoplasmic organisms evolved
out of the elemental ooze. All vertebrates have
nerve-filled backbones with two pairs of ventrally
branching limbs, because the original ancestors of
the vertebrates had nerve-filled backbones with
two pairs of ventrally branching limbs. Insects
individually evolve from worms because worms
are their phylogenetic fathers and mothers. Man
has hands and a vertical spine, and walks on his
hind-limbs, not because he was fashioned in the
image of a god, but because his ancestors lived
among the trees. The habit of using the posterior
limbs for locomotion, and the anterior for prehension, and the resulting perpendicular, are

peculiarities developed by our simian ancestors wholly on account of the incentives to such structure and posture afforded by aboreal life. These peculiarities would not likely have been acquired by quadrupeds living upon and taking their food from a perfectly level and treeless plain. If there had been no forests on the earth, therefore, there would have been no incentive to the perpendicular, and the 'human form divine' would have been inconceivably different from what it is to-day. And if fishes had had three serial pairs of limbs instead of two, and their posterity had inherited them, as they certainly would have had the foresight to do if they had had the opportunity, the highest animals on the earth to-day, the 'paragons of creation,' would probably be two-handed quadrupeds (centaurs) instead of two-handed bipeds. And much more efficient and ideal individuals they would have been in every way than the rickety, peculiar, unsubstantial plantigrades who, by their talent to talk, have become the masters of the universe, and, by their imaginations, 'divine.'

Kinship is universal. The orders, families, species, and races of the animal kingdom are the branches of a gigantic arbour. Every individual is a cell, every species is a tissue, and every order is an organ in the great surging, suffering, palpitating process. Man is simply one portion of the immense enterprise. He is as veritably an animal as the insect that drinks its little fill from his veins, the ox he goads, or the wild-fox that flees before his bellowings. Man is not a god, nor in any imminent danger of becoming one. He is not a celestial star-babe dropped down among mundane matters for a time and endowed with wing possibilities and the anatomy of a deity. He is a mammal of the order of primates, not so lamentable when we think of the hyena and the serpent, but an exceedingly discouraging vertebrate compared with what he ought to be. He has come up from the worm and the quadruped. His relatives dwell on the prairies and in the fields, forests, and waves. He shares the honours and partakes of the infirmities of all his kindred. He walks on his hind-limbs like the ape; he eats herbage and suckles his young like the ox; he slays his fellows and fills himself with their blood like the crocodile and the tiger; he grows old and dies, and turns to banqueting worms, like all that come from the elemental loins. He cannot exceed the winds like the hound, nor dissolve his image in the mid-day blue like the eagle. He has not the courage of the gorilla, the magnificence of the steed, nor the plaintive innocence of the ring-dove. Poor, pitiful, glory-hunting hideful! Born into a universe which he creates when he comes into it, and clinging, like all his kindred, to a clod that knows him not, he drives on in the preposterous storm of the atoms, as helpless to fashion his fate as the sleet that pelts him, and lost absolutely in the somnambulism of his own being.

BIBLIOGRAPHY

(1) HARTMANN : Anthropoid Apes ; New York, 1901.

(2) QUATREFAGES : The Human Species ; New York, 1898.

(3) TYLOR : Anthropology ; New York, 1899.

(4) HAECKEL : History of Creation, 2 vols.; New York, 1896.

(5) HAECKEL : The Riddle of the Universe; New York, 1901.

(6) HUXLEY : Man's Place in Nature ; New York, 1883.

(7) JORDAN : Footnotes of Evolution ; New York, 1898.

(8) DARWIN : Descent of Man, 2nd edit.; London, 1874.

(9) DRUMMOND : Ascent of Man ; New York, 1894.

(10) THOMPSON : Outlines of Zoology, 3rd edit. ; Edinburgh, 1899.

(11) HUXLEY : On the Origin of Species, lecture iv.

THE PSYCHICAL KINSHIP

' I saw, deep in the eyes of the animals, the human soul look out upon me.

' I saw where it was born down deep under feathers and fur, or condemned for awhile to roam four-footed among the brambles. I caught the clinging mute glance of the prisoner, and swore that I would be faithful.

' Thee, my brother and sister, I see and mistake not. Do not be afraid. Dwelling thus and thus for awhile, fulfilling thy appointed time—thou too shalt come to thyself at last.

' Thy half-warm horns and long tongue lapping round my wrist do not conceal thy humanity any more than the learned talk of the pedant conceals his—for all thou art dumb we have words and plenty between us.'—EDWARD CARPENTER.

THE PSYCHICAL KINSHIP

I. The Conflict of Science and Tradition.

THE doctrine that on mankind's account all other beings came into existence, and that non-human beings are mere hunks of matter devoid of all psychic qualities found in man, is a doctrine about as sagacious as the old geocentric theory of the universe. Conceit is a distinctly human emotion. No other animal has it. But it has been lavished upon man with a generosity sufficient to compensate for its total absence from the rest of the universe. Man has always overestimated himself. In whatever age or province of the world you look down on the human imagination, you find it industriously digging disparities and establishing gulfs. Man, according to himself, has had great difficulty many times in the history of the world in escaping the divine. According to the facts, he has only in recent biological times and after great labour and uncertainty abandoned his tail and his all-fours. According to himself, man was made 'in the image of his maker,' and has been endowed with powers and properties peculiarly his own. According to the facts, he has come into the world in a manner identical with that of all other animals, and has been endowed with like nature and destiny. Man has never manifested a warmer or more indelicate enthusiasm than the enthusiasm with which he has appreciated himself. And with the same ardour with which he has praised himself he has maligned and misrepresented others. Man has set himself up as the supreme judge and executive of the world, and he has not hesitated to award to himself the lion's share of everything. He has ransacked his fancy for adjectives with which to praise himself, and driven his inventive faculties to the verge of distraction in search of justification for his crimes upon those around him. Every individual bent on deeds of darkness first seeks in his own mind justification for his purposed sins. And it is a caustic comment on the character of human conviction that no enthusiastic criminal— from the marauder of continents to the kitchen pilferer—ever yet sought unsuccessfully at the court of his conscience for a sinful permit. It was an easy matter, therefore, for man—aided as he was by such an experienced imagination—to convince himself that all other animals were made for him, that they were made without feeling or intelligence, and that hence he was justified in using in any way he chose the conveniences so generously provided by an eccentric providence.

But Darwin has lived. Beings have come into the world, we now know, through the operation of

natural law.   Man is not different from the rest.
The story of Eden is a fabrication, bequeathed to
us by our well-meaning but dimly-lighted ancestors.
There has been no more miracle in the origin of
the human species than in the origin of any other
species.   And there is no more miracle in the origin
of a species than there is in the birth of a molecule
or in the breaking of a tired wave on the beach.
Man was not made in the image of the hypothetical
creator of heaven and earth, but in the image of
the ape.   Man is not a fallen god, but a promoted reptile.   The beings around him are not
conveniences, but cousins.   Instead of stretching
away to the stars, man's pedigree slinks down into
the sea.   Horrible revelation!   Frightful anti-
thesis!   Instead of celestial genesis and a 'fall'
—long and doleful promotion.   Instead of elysian
gardens and romance—the slime.   Instead of a
god with royal nostrils miraculously animating an
immortal duplicate—a little lounging cellule, too
small to be seen and too senseless to distinguish
between midnight and noon.   But the situation is
not half so horrible as it looks to be to those who
see only the skin of things.   Is it not better, after
all, to be the honourable outcome of a straightforward evolution than the offspring of flunky-
loving celestials?   Are the illustrious children of
the ape less glorious than the sycophants of
irrational theological systems?   Darwin dealt in
his quiet way some malicious blows to human
conceit, but he also bequeathed to a misguided
world the elements of its ultimate redemption.

The supposed psychical gulf between human and non-human beings has no more existence, outside the flamboyant imagination of man, than has the once-supposed physical gulf. It is pure fiction. The supposition is a relic of the rapidly dwindling vanity of anthropocentricism, and is perpetuated from age to age by human selfishness and conceit. It has no foundation either in science or in common-sense. Man strives to lessen his guilt by the laudation of himself and the disparagement and degradation of his victims. Like the ostrich, who, pursued by death, improvises an imaginary escape by plunging its head into the desert, so man, pursued by the vengeful correctives of his own conscience, fabricates a fictitious innocence by the calumniation of those upon whom he battens. But such excuses cannot much longer hold out against the rising consciousness of kinship. Psychology, like all other sciences, is rapidly ceasing to attend exclusively to human phenomena. It is lifting up its eyes and looking about ; it is preparing to become comparative. It has come to realise that the mind of man is but a single shoot of a something which ramifies the entire animal world, and that in order to understand its subject it is necessary for it to familiarise itself with the whole field of phenomenon. The soul of man did not commence to be in the savage. It commenced to be in the worm, whose life man grinds out with his heel, and in the bivalve that flounders in his broth. The roots of consciousness are in the sea. Side by side with physical evolution has gone on psychical evolution; side by side with the evolution of organs and tissues has gone on the evolution of intellect, sensibility, and will. Human nature and human mind are no more *sui generis* than are human anatomy and physiology. The same considerations that prove that man's material organism is the cumulative result of long evolution proclaim that human mind, the immaterial concomitant of the material organism, is also the cumulative result of long evolution.

We might just as well recognise facts first as last, for they will have to be recognised some time. Truths are not put down by inhospitality—they are simply put off. The universe has a policy, a program. We may close our eyes to the facts around us, hoping in this way to compel them to pass away or be forgotten. But they do not pass away, nor will they be forgotten. They simply become invisible. They will live on and present themselves to other minds or ages or climes more hospitable or honest than our own. The only proper attitude of mind to assume toward the various doctrines existing among men is the attitude of perfect willingness to believe *anything*—anything that appeals to us as being reasonable and right. The great majority of men, however, are intellectual solids—unable to move and un-willing to think. They have certain beliefs *to which they are determined to hold on,* and everything that does not fit in with these beliefs is rejected as a matter of course.

II. Evidences of Psychical Evolution.

That mind has evolved, and that there is a psychical kinship, an actual consanguinity of feelings and ideas, among all the forms of animal life is proved incontestably by the following facts:

1. The evolution of mind is implied by the fact of the evolution of structures. 'I hold,' says Romanes, in the introduction to his great work on 'Mental Evolution,' 'that, if the doctrine of organic evolution is accepted, it carries with it, as a necessary corollary, the doctrine of mental evolution.' It makes no difference what theory we adopt regarding the essential natures of the physical and the psychical—whether we agree with the materialist that mind is an attribute of matter, with the idealist that matter is a creation of mind, with the monist that mind and body are only different aspects of the same central entity, or with the dualist that body and soul are two distinct but temporarily dependent existences—we must in any case recognise the fact, which is perceived by all, that there is an ever-faithful parallel between the neural and psychical phenomena of every organism. And if the elements which enter into and make up the physical structure of man have been derived from, and determined by, preceding forms of life, the elements which enter into and make up the psychical counterpart of the physical have also, without any doubt, been inherited from, and determined by, ancestral life forms.

2. Closely allied to the foregoing reason for a belief in the evolution of mind is that derived from a comparative survey of the nervous system in man and other animals. In man, mind is closely associated with a certain tissue or system of tissues—*nerve tissue* or *the nervous system*. That mind is correlated with nerve structure, and that mental anatomy may be learned from a study of the anatomy of the nervous system, especially of the brain, is the basic postulate of the science of physiological psychology. Now, nerve cells exist in all animals above the sponge, and a comparatively well-developed nervous system is found even among many of the invertebrates, as the higher worms, crustaceans, insects, and mollusks. The nervous system of invertebrates, though composed of the same kind of tissue, is constructed according to a somewhat different plan of architecture from that of the vertebrates. But in all of the great family of backboned animals the nervous system is built on the same general plan as in man, with a cerebro-spinal trunk extending from the head along the back and motory and sensory nerves ramifying to all parts of the body. There is also a sympathetic nervous system in all animals down as far as the insects. The brain, which is the most important part of the nervous system, and which has been called the 'organ of consciousness,' presents throughout the animal kingdom, from its beginning in the worms to man, a graduated series of increasing complication proceeding out of the same fundamental type. This is especially

true of the vertebrates. Fishes, amphibians, reptiles, birds, and mammals, all have in their brains the same primary parts, the same five fundamental divisions, as are found in the brain of man. Hence, whatever may be thought about the mental states of invertebrates, we have the right, in the case of the vertebrate orders of life, to infer, from the general similarity of their nervous system to our own, that they have a corresponding similarity to ourselves in mental constitution and experience.

3. The evolution of mind is suggested by the existence in the animal world of all grades of intelligence, from almost mindless forms to forms even exceeding in some respects the mental attainments of men. The jelly-fish and the philosopher are not mental aliens. They are linked to each other by a continuous gradation of intermediate intelligences. The existence of these grades of mental development suggest psychical evolution and kinship, just as the existence of like grades of structural development suggest physical evolution.

4. In the mental life of animals the same factors of evolution exist as those by means of which organic structures have been brought into existence, and it is reasonable to suppose that the operation of these factors have produced in the mental world results analogous to those produced by the operation of the same factors among organic structures.

Men and other animals *vary* in their natures

and mental faculties quite as much as they do in colour, size, and shape. It is commonly supposed that the mental and temperamental variety existing among individual men does not exist among individual birds, quadrupeds, insects, etc. But a little observation or reflection ought to be enough to convince anyone that such a supposition belongs to that batch of pre-Darwinian mistakes presented to us by an over-generous past. We are *not acquainted* with the inhabitants of our fields and barn-yards. We are almost as ignorant of the mental life and personality of these door-yard neighbours and friends of ours as we would be if they were the inhabitants of another continent. That is why our obtuse minds lump them together so indiscriminately—we do not know anything about them. We never take the trouble, or think it worth while, to get acquainted with them, much less to study and know them. We have grown up in the falsehood that they are altogether different from what we are, and that it is really not worth while to bother our gigantic heads about them, except to use them when it comes handy, or kick them to one side, or execute them, when they get in the way. Everybody else looks at the matter in about the same way, so we just let it go at that.

There is a sameness about foreigners and other classes of *human* beings with whom we are but slightly, or not at all, acquainted, until we come to know them and can discriminate one from another. I remember once asking my sister, if her baby, which looked to me like all other babies I had ever seen, were mixed up with a lot of other babies of about the same age, whether she could pick hers out from all the rest, and she gave me an unmistakable affirmative by answering, ' What a foolish question !'

There is less variety among the individuals of non-human races than among individual men, just as there is less variety among individual savages than among the members of a civilised community.   But there is mental diversity among all beings, and we only need to whittle our observation a little to recognise the fact.   You never hear the keeper of a menagerie or any intelligent associate of dogs, horses, birds, or insects say there is no individuality among these animals. Brehm, the great German naturalist, assures us that each individual monkey of all those he kept tame in Africa had its own peculiar temper and disposition.   And this is no more than what everyone who knows anything about it knows to be true of dogs, horses, cats, cattle, birds, and even fishes and insects.   Any intelligent dog-fancier or pigeon-fancier can tell you the personal peculiarities of every one of the fifty or a hundred dogs or pigeons in his charge.   He has watched and studied them since they came into existence, and through this continuous association he has come to *know* them.   He simply makes discriminations that are not made by the casual or superficial observer.   The Laplander knows and names each reindeer in his herd, though to a stranger they are all as much alike as the multitudes on an ant-hill. The Peckhams of Milwaukee, those indefatigable investigators of spiders and insects, are constantly telling us of the wonderful individuality possessed by these lowly lessees of our fields and gardens. In their work on ' The Habits and Instincts of the Solitary Wasps,' speaking of the ammophiles, these authors say : ' In this species, as in every one that we have studied, we have found a most interesting variation among the different individuals, not only in methods, but in character and intellect. While one was beguiled from her hunting by every sorrel blossom she passed, another stuck to her work with indefatigable perseverance. While one stung her caterpillars so carelessly and made her nest in so shiftless a way that her young could survive only through some lucky chance, another devoted herself to these duties not only with conscientious earnestness, but with an apparent craving after artistic perfection that was touching to see.' The variation in the mental phenomena of animals, including man, is partly innate, and partly the result of environment or education.

Animals not only vary in their mental qualities, but they also *inherit* these variations, just as they do physical properties and peculiarities. Evidence of this is furnished by every new being that comes into the world. Insanity runs in families, and so does genius and criminality. Even the most trifling idiosyncrasies are often transmitted, not only by men, but also by dogs, horses, and other animals. Such qualities of mind as courage, fidelity, good and bad temper, intelligence, timidity, special tastes and aptitudes, are certainly transmitted in all the higher orders of animal life.

Animals are also *selected*, are enabled to survive in the struggle for life quite as much through the possession by them of certain mental qualities as on account of their physical characters. Whether the selections are made by nature or by man, they are not determined by the physical facts of size, strength, speed, and the like, more than by cunning, courage, sagacity, skill, industry, devotion, ferocity, tractability, and other mental properties. The fittest survive, and the fittest may be the most timid or analytic as well as the most powerful. No better illustration of this truth can be found than that furnished by man himself. Man is by nature a comparatively feeble animal. He is neither large nor powerful. Yet he has been selected to prosper over all other animals because of his ingenuity, sympathy, and art. The great feeling and civilisation of higher men have been built up by slow accretion due to the operation of the law of survival extending over vast measures of time. Creeds and instincts, governments and impulses, forms of thought and forms of expression, have struggled and survived just as have cells and species. A struggle for existence is constantly going on, as Max Müller has pointed out, even among the words and grammatical forms of every language. The better, shorter, easier forms are constantly gaining the ascendancy, and the longer and more cumbrous expressions grow obsolete.

If, therefore, the higher types of mind have not come into existence as have the higher types of structure, through evolution from simpler and more generalised forms, it has not been due to the absence of the factors necessary for bringing about this evolution.

5. The presumption created by the existence of the factors of psychic evolution is strengthened by the facts of artificial selection. We *know* mind *can* evolve, *for it has done so in many cases.* The races of domesticated animals, the races whom man has exploited and preyed upon during the past several thousand years, have, many of them, been completely changed in character and intelligence through human selection. Old instincts have been wiped out and new ones implanted. In many instances the psychology has been not only revolutionised, but remade.

Take, for instance, the dog. The dog is a reformed bandit. It is a revised wolf or jackal. It has been completely transformed by human selection; indeed, it may be said that the dog in the last ten or fifteen thousand years has made greater advances in sagacity and civilisation than any other animal, scarcely even excepting man. Man has made wonderful strides along purely intellectual lines, but in the improvement of his emotions he has not been so successful. The rapid development of the dog in feeling and intelligence has no doubt been due to the fact that his utility to man has always depended largely on his good sense and fidelity, and man has persistently emphasised these qualities in his selection. Fierceness and distrust—two of the most prominent traits in the psychology of the primitive dog—have been entirely eradicated in the higher races of dogs. There is not anywhere on the face of the earth a more trustful, affectionate, and docile being than this one-time cut-throat. Whether the dog has been derived from the wolf or from some wild canine race now extinct, or from several distinct ancestors, he must have had originally a fierce, distrustful, and barbaric nature, for all of the undomesticated members of the dog family—wolves, foxes, jackals, etc.—have natures of this sort.

There are about 175 different races of domestic dogs. They represent almost as great a range of development as do the races of men. Some of them are exceedingly primitive, while others are highly intelligent and civilised. The Eskimo dogs are really nothing but wolves that have been trained to the service of man. They look like wolves, and have the wolf psychology. They are not able to bark, like ordinary dogs; they howl like wolves, and their ears stand up straight, like the ears of all wild Canidæ. Some of the more advanced of the canine races—like the sheep-dogs, pointers, and St. Bernards—are animals of great sympathy and sensibility. When educated, these dogs are almost human in their impulses and in their powers of discernment. In patience, vigilance, and devotion to duty, they are superior to many men. At a word, or even a look, from its master, the loyal collie will gather the sheep scattered for miles around to the place designated, and do it with such tact and expedition as to command admiration. It has been said that if it were not for this faithful and competent canine the highlands of Scotland would be almost useless for sheep-raising purposes, because of the greater expense that would be entailed if men were employed. One collie will do the work of several men, and will do it better, and the generous-hearted creature pours out its services like water. It requires no compensation except table refuse and a straw bed. In South America sheep-dogs are trained to act as shepherds and assume the whole responsibility of tending the flock. ' It is a common thing,' says Darwin, ' to meet a large flock of sheep guarded by one or two dogs, at a distance of some miles from any house or man.' When the dogs get hungry, they come home for food, but immediately return to the flock on being fed. ' It is amusing,' remarks this writer, ' to observe, when approaching a flock, how the dog immediately advances barking, while the sheep all close in his rear as around the oldest ram.'

Romanes relates an incident which well illustrates the high character and intelligence of the dog and its wonderful devotion to a trust. ' It was a Scotch collie. Her master was in the habit of consigning sheep to her charge without supervision. On this particular occasion he remained behind or proceeded by another road. On arriving at home late in the evening, he was astonished to learn that his faithful animal had not made her appearance with the drove. He immediately set out in search of her. But on going out into the streets, there she was coming with the drove, not one missing, and, marvellous to relate, she was carrying a young puppy in her mouth. She had been taken in travail on the hills, and how the poor creature had contrived to manage her drove in her condition is beyond human calculation, for her road lay through sheep all the way. Her master's heart smote him when he saw what she had suffered and effected. But she was nothing daunted, and after depositing her young one in a place of safety she again set out full speed for the hills, and brought another and another, till she brought the whole litter, one by one ; but the last one was dead '(1).

What a wonderful transformation in canine character ! The very beings whose blood the dog once drank with ravenous thirst it now protects with courage and fidelity. And this transformation in character is not due to education simply. It is innate. Young dogs brought from Tierra del Fuego or Australia, where the natives do not keep such domestic animals as sheep, pigs, and poultry, invariably have an incurable propensity for attacking these animals.

The feeling of ownership possessed by so many dogs is an entirely new element in canine character, a trait implanted wholly by human selection.

Bold and confident on his own premises, the dog immediately becomes weak and apologetic when placed in circumstances in which he feels he has no rights.

The pointers and setters have been developed as distinct breeds by human selection during the past 150 or 200 years.

What is true of the dog is true also, to a large extent, of the cat, cow, horse, sheep, goat, fowl, and other domestic animals. Serene and peaceful puss is the tranquillised descendant of the wild cat of Egypt, one of the most untamable of all animals. The migratory instinct, so strong in wild water-fowl, is almost absent from our geese and ducks, as is the fighting propensity (prominent in the Indian jungle-bird) from most varieties of the domesticated chicken. There are now as many as a hundred different kinds of domesticated animals, and there is scarcely one of these animals that has not been profoundly changed in character during the period of its domestication. There are much greater changes in some races than in others. Some races have been much longer in captivity than others. And then, too, there is great difference in the degree of plasticity in different races, the races of ancient origin being much more fixed in their psychology than those of more recent beginnings. In some races, too—as in the sheep —the selections made by man have been made primarily with reference to certain physical qualities, and in these cases the mental qualities have been only incidentally affected. In Polynesia, where it is selected for its flavour instead of for its fleetness or intelligence, the dog is said to be a very stupid animal. But in most cases of domestication the changes wrought by selection in the mental make-up of the race have been fully as great as the changes in body, and in some instances much greater. And the process by which these great changes in psychology have been effected is in principle identically the same as that by which mental evolution in general is assumed to have been brought about.

6. The evolution of mind in the animal world in general is suggested by the fact that mind in man has evolved. The rich, luminous intellect of civilised man, with its art, science, law, literature, government, and morality, has been evolved from the rude, raw, demon-haunted mind of the savage. Evidence of this evolution is furnished by the recorded facts of human history, by the antiquarian collections of our museums, and by a study of existing savages.

History everywhere has come out of the night, out of the deep gloom of the unrecorded. But it has not leaped forth like lightning out of the darkness. It has dawned, night being succeeded by the amorphous shadows of legend and tradition, and these in turn by the attested events of true history. Almost every civilised people can trace back its genealogy to a time when it was represented on the earth by one or more tribes of savage or half-savage ancestors. The Anglo-Saxons go back to the Angles, Saxons, and Jutes, three semi-savage tribes who came to England from the borderlands of the Baltic fourteen or fifteen centuries ago.   The French are the descendants cf the Gauls, who formed the scattered population of warring and superstitious tribes referred to by Julius Cæsar in the opening lines of his ' Commentaries.' The blue-eyed Germans came from the Cimbri, the Goths, and the Vandals, those bold, wild hordes who charged out of the north to battle with the power of Rome.   And all of the Aryan races — English, German, Italian, Scandinavian, Russian, Roman, Greek, and Persian —trace their ancestry back, by means of common languages and legends, to a time when they were wandering tribes of nomads tenting somewhere on the plains of transcaspian Asia.

In all our museums there are collections of the relics of prehistoric peoples.   These. collections consist of objects upon which men in distant ages of the world have wrought—their weapons, ornaments, utensils, implements, and playthings — which have been saved from the teeth of Time by their durability.   The character of the minds which operated on these objects, which produced and used them, may be inferred from the character of the objects, just as the life and surroundings of an ancient animal or plant may be inferred from its fossil.   These relics are of stone, bone, bronze, and iron.   They are found in almost every region of the earth—all over Europe and its islands, in western and central Asia, in China and Japan, in Malay, Australia, and New Zealand, in the islands of the Pacific, and throughout the length and breadth of America. They antedate human history by thousands of years. They are the ruins of the Stone Age, the Bronze Age, and the Iron Age of mankind. In all of these remains there is evidence of a slow but gradual improvement as we approach the present. There are places on the earth where the evolution of human implements, from the rudest chipped stones to the comparatively finished products of historic peoples, is epitomised in the deposits of a few feet in depth. One of these occurs at Chelles, a suburb of Paris, and was made the subject of a paper by Professor Packard in the *Popular Science Monthly* for May, 1902. Here three distinct layers, containing human remains entirely different in character from each other, appear within a depth of 30 feet from the surface. The lowest bed, a layer of pebbles and sand, and probably preglacial in origin, contains the famous Chellean ' axes,' rude almond-shaped implements of chipped flint, and used by these ancient inhabitants by being held in the hand. In this bed are also found the bones of the straight-tusked elephant, cave-bear, big-nosed rhinoceros, and other species now extinct. The next bed is the interglacial, and contains implements entirely different from the one below it, among which are skin-scrapers and lance-points. The animal remains of this bed are also different from those found in the bed below, and include animals like the musk-ox and the reindeer, which were probably driven to this southern clime from more northern regions by the excessive cold of the time. The third bed, which lies just below the surface soils, contains polished stone axes and other remains of human industry cotemporaneous with the Swiss lake-dwellers. From the swamps and loams are sometimes dug up the remains of Gallo-Roman civilisations—Gallic coins, serpentine axes, and bronzes of the time of the Antonines.

No one can fully realise the vast advance that has been made by the human mind until he has looked upon a savage—has seen the savage in his native haunts attacking the problems of his daily life, and has tasted of his philosophy and disposition. The savage is the ancestor of all higher men. When we look upon the savage, we look upon the infancy of the human world. All of the laws, languages, sciences, governments, religions, and philosophies of civilised man, or nearly all of them at any rate, are the exfoliated laws, languages, sciences, governments, religions, and philosophies of savages. It is impossible to understand the laws of civilised societies without a knowledge of the laws of savage societies. The same thing is true of government, religion, and philosophy— and of human nature itself. Human nature as exhibited by civilised men and women—I mean men and women with a veneering of civility, not really civilised folks, for there are none of them on the earth—is a perpetual enigma unless it is illumined by restrospection, by a comparative study of human nature, by a study of human nature as seen in more and more primitive men

and women. The mind of the savage, as compared with that of civilised man, is exceedingly
primitive. The picture drawn by Gilbraith of the
North American Sioux is a typical picture of
savage life and character. Gilbraith lived among
these tribes for several years, and was thoroughly
acquainted with them. He says:

'They are bigoted, barbarous, and exceedingly
superstitious. They regard most of the vices as
virtues. Theft, arson, rape, and murder are regarded by them as the means of distinction. The
young Indian is taught from childhood to regard
killing as the highest of virtues. In their dances
and at their feasts, the warriors recite their deeds
of theft, pillage, and slaughter as precious things;
and the highest, indeed the only, ambition of the
young brave is to secure " the feather," which is
but the record of his having murdered, or partici-
pated in the murder of, some human being—
whether man, woman, or child, it is immaterial' (19).

'Conscience,' says Burton, 'does not exist in
East Africa, and "repentance" simply expresses
regret for missed opportunities for crime. Robbery
makes an honorable man; and murder, the more
atrocious the crime the better, makes the hero' (2).

Many things appear natural and self-evident to
the savage which seem to us actually revolting.
When the Fuegians are hard pressed by want,
they kill their old women for food rather than
their dogs, saying: 'Old women no use; dogs
kill otters.' 'What!' said a negro to Burton,

' am I to starve while my sister has children whom she can sell ?'

Lubbock, in his great work on ' The Origin of Civilisation,' cites hundreds of instances of savage rudeness and simplicity which seem almost incredible to one accustomed all his life to types of human character such as are found in Europe and America. For instance, ' when the natives of the Lower Murray first saw pack-oxen, some of them were frightened and took them for demons with spears on their heads, while others thought they were the wives of the settlers, because they carried the baggage.' Speaking of the wild men in the interior of Borneo, this writer says : ' They live absolutely in a state of nature, neither cultivating the ground nor living in huts. They eat neither rice nor salt, and do not associate with each other, but rove about the woods like wild beasts. The sexes meet in the jungle. When the children are old enough to shift for themselves, they usually separate, neither one afterwards thinking of the other. At night they sleep under some large tree whose branches hang low. They fasten the children to the branches in a kind of swing, and build a fire around the tree to protect them from snakes and wild beasts. The poor creatures are looked on and treated by the other Dyaks as wild beasts.' Lubbock sums up his conclusions on the morality of savages in the following pathetic acknowledgment : ' I do not remember a single instance in which a savage is recorded as having shown any symptoms of remorse ; and almost the only case I can call to mind in which a man belonging to one of the lower races has accounted for an act by saying explicitly that it was right, was when Mr. Hunt asked a young Figian why he had killed his mother' (3).

A few pages further on, the same author adds, regarding the deplorable state of morality among savages : ' That there should be races of men so deficient in moral feeling was altogether opposed to the preconceived ideas with which I commenced the study of savage life, and I have arrived at the conviction by slow degrees, and even with reluctance. I have, however, been forced to this conclusion, not only by the direct statements of travellers, but also by the general tenor of their remarks, and especially by the remarkable absence of repentance and remorse among the lowest races of men.' Among ourselves the words used to distinguish right and wrong are metaphors. *Right* originally meant ' straight,' and *wrong* meant ' twisted.' Language existed, therefore, before morality ; for if moral ideas had preceded language, there would have been *original words* to stand for them. Religion, according to Lubbock, has no moral aspect or influence except among the more advanced races of men. ' The deities of savages are evil, not good; they may be forced into compliance with the wishes of man ; they generally delight in bloody, and often require human, sacrifices ; they are mortal, not immortal ; they are to be approached by dances rather than by prayers ; and often approve what we call vice rather than what we esteem as virtue. In fact, the so-called religion of the lower races of mankind bears somewhat the same relation to religion in its higher forms as astrology does to astronomy or alchemy to chemistry ' (3).

Savages have few general ideas of any kind, as is evidenced by the almost total absence among them of words denoting general ideas. Many savage races cannot comprehend numbers greater than five or six, and are unable to make the simplest mathematical computations without using the fingers. The languages of savages are extremely rude, words being freely pieced out with pantomime. Savages talk with difficulty in the dark, because of their great reliance on gesture in conversation. The rich vocabularies of the languages of Europe and America have grown up step by step with the evolution of European and American mind. Every language is an evolution. The languages of many primitive peoples lack the verb *to be* entirely, and all nouns are proper nouns. Words are often little more than grunts or clucks, and are without the euphony and articulation found in the languages of the civilised. Darwin says that the language of the Fuegians sounds like a man clearing his throat. Not only every language, but every word, both in its form and meaning, is in process of evolution. *Spirit*, for instance, originally meant ' blowing,' *understanding* meant ' getting beneath,' and *development* the physical act of 'unfolding.' Words are continually drifting from their original meanings under the stress of incessant use, as ships drag their anchors in a gale. Those words that are exposed to common use undergo the most rapid changes, while words sheltered from the rush of human affairs, like harboured ships, hold to their moorings forever. *Let*, for instance, once meant 'hinder'; now it means 'allow.' *Bisect*, on the other hand, a word of rare and technical use, has remained unaltered in significance for twenty centuries.

Even our alphabet has been evolved. The twenty-six symbols composing it have been eroded into the peculiar forms in which they appear at present by the various peoples through whose hands they have come to us. The originals were pictographs such as are still found on the aged monuments of earth's earliest civilisations. The English got their alphabet from the Romans, who obtained it, along with almost everything else they had, from the Greeks. The Greeks received it from the Phenicians, and the Phenicians from the papyrus writers of Egypt, who in turn procured it from those hieroglyph chiselers who carved their curious literatures on the granite tombs of the Nile in the remotest dawn of human history. *A*, the first letter of our alphabet, is a figure which has been evolved, as the result of long wear and tear, from the picture of an eagle; *B* was originally the picture of a crane; *C* represents a throne; *D* a hand; *F* an asp; *H* a sieve; *K* a bowl; *L* a lioness; *M* an owl; *N* a water-line; *R* a mouth; *S* a garden; *T* a lassoo; *X* a chairback; and *Z* a duck.

The psychology of civilised man, though derived from that of the savage, and hence resembling it fundamentally, is, nevertheless, very different from it, both in character and in what it contains. The mind of the savage is rude, unresourceful, vicious, and childlike, while that of the civilised man or woman may be overflowing with wisdom and benignity. This gulf has not been covered by a stride, but by the slow operation of the same laws of Inheritance, Variation, and Selection by which all progress has been brought about.

7. Degeneration is a necessary part of the process of organic evolution. All progress, whether anatomical, intellectual, or social, takes place through selection, and selection means the pining and ultimate passing away of that which is left. In individual evolution it is organs, ideas, and traits of character that are eliminated, and in social evolution it is customs and institutions. One of the reasons given in the preceding chapter for the belief in the evolution of structures is the existence in man and other animals of *vestigial organs*, organs which in lower forms of life are useful, but which in higher forms are represented by useless or even injurious remnants. Similar remnants are found in the *psychology* of man and other animals. These vestiges of mind are not so easily recognised as the vestiges of structure, but they are everywhere. We find them in the antiquated instincts of man and the domestic animals, in the silent letters and worn-out words

of languages, and in the emaciated remains of abandoned beliefs and institutions.

The hunting and fishing instinct of civilised man is a vestigial instinct, normal in the savage, but without either sense or decency among men devoted to industrial pursuits. The savage hunts and fishes because he is hungry, never for pastime; civilised men and women do so because they are too mechanical to assort their impulses. Civilised man is a mongrel, a cross between a barbarian and a god. His psychology is a compound of the jungle and the sky. In their loftier moments, many men are able to obscure the cruder facts of their origin and to put into temporary operation those more splendid processes of mind which characterise their ideals. But even the most civilised are forever haunted by the returning ghosts of departed propensities—propensities which grew up in ages of hate, which are now out-of-date, but which in the trying tedium of daily life come back and usurp the high places in human nature. Revenge, hate, cruelty, pugnacity, selfishness, vanity, and the like, are all more or less vestigial among men who have entered seriously on the life of altruism. Like the vermiform appendix and the human tail, these old obsolete parts of the human mind are destined, in the ripening of the ages, to waste away and disappear through disuse.

The practice of the dog of turning round two or three times before lying down is in response to an instinct which was no doubt beneficial to it in its wild life, when it was wont to make its bed in the grasses, but which is now a pure waste of time. Darwin records it as a fact, that he has himself seen a simple-minded dog turn round twenty times before lying down. The sheep-killing mania, which sometimes comes over dogs when three or four of them get together and become actuated by the ' mob ' spirit, is a vestige of the old instinct of the carnivore which centuries of domestication have not yet quite erased. Goodness, if too prolonged, becomes irksome to dogs for the same reason that it does to men. Dogs have come from savages just as men have, and, while the civilised nature of the dog is more constitutional than that of civilised man, the old deposed instincts mount to the throne once in awhile, and the faithful collie is for the time being a wolf again. The instinct of domestic sheep to imitate their leader in leaping over obstacles is another probable survival of wild life. If a bar or other obstacle be placed where the leader of a flock of sheep is compelled to leap over it, and the obstacle is then removed, the entire band of followers will leap at the same place regardless of the fact that the obstruction is no longer there. No other animals do this. The instinct is probably a survival of wild life, when these animals, pursued by their enemies over chasms and precipices, were compelled to imitate in the flight those in front of them in order to live. Darwin thinks the donkey shows its aboriginal desert nature in its aversion for crossing the smallest stream, and its relish for rolling in the dust. The same aversion for everything aquatic exists also in the camel. Quails kept in captivity, I am told, persist in scratching at the pan when they are feeding, just as they would need to do, and were accustomed to do, among the leaves and grasses of the groves. The restlessness of cage-birds and domestic fowls at migrating time, the mimic dipping and sporting of ducks when confined to a terrestrial habitat, the grave marshalling of geese by the chief gander of the band, the ferocity of cows, ewes, and the females of other domestic animals during the first few days of motherhood, the hunting instinct of dogs kept as shepherds and pets, the squatting of young pigs when suddenly alarmed—all of these are vestigial instincts, functional in the wild state, but now useless and absurd.

The silent letters and superannuated words and phrases found everywhere in literature are the vestigial parts of language. Every silent letter was originally sounded, and every obsolete word was at one time used. In the French word, *temps*, for instance, which means 'time,' neither the *p* nor the *s* is sounded. But in the Latin word *tempus*, from which the French word is derived, all of the letters are sounded.

Man has been defined as a creature of habit. As he has done a thing once, or as his ancestors have done a thing, so he does it again. By precept and example he transmits to each new generation the customs, beliefs, and points of view which he has invented. Social changes take place with extreme moderation. The drowsy ages take plenty of time to get anywhere. Civilisation is lazy, deliberate, unimpassioned. It loafs and hesitates. It holds on to the past. Living civilisations always drag behind them a trail of traditions from dead civilisations. Religions and philosophies change, and creeds and governments flow into strange and undreamed-of forms; but their personalities survive, their souls live on, their remnants, transmitted as traditions from generation to generation, defy the meddlings of innovators. Hence in every society there are forms and ceremonies, laws and customs, games and symbols, etc., which have been completely diverted from their original purposes, or which have become so reduced in importance as to be of no use. Spencer has shown that the forms of salutation in vogue among civilised societies are the vestiges of primitive ceremonial used to denote submission. The May Day festivals with which the opening spring is usually hailed are the much-modified survivals of pagan festivals in honour of plant and animal fecundity. Superstition and folklore are vestigial opinions. The gorgeous Easter egg is a survival of a dawn myth older than the Pyramids, and our Christmas dinner is a reminiscence of a cannibal carnival celebrating the turning back of the sun at the winter solstice (Brinton). In the English government, where democracy has in recent centuries made such inroads on the monarchy, there are numerous examples of vestigial institutions—institutions which continue to exist purely because they have existed in the past, but which were functional a few centuries ago. The supreme office itself is one of these. The King represents the petered-out tail-end of a privilege which in the time of the early Stuarts was almost unlimited. Similar vestiges exist in the United States, where the national spirit during the last century and a half has so completely wiped out colonialism. Such are the Town Meetings of Boston and of New Haven. The earliest form of human marriage was marriage by capture. The man stole the woman and carried her away by force. This form of marriage was in the course of evolution succeeded by marriage through purchase. A man anxious to become a husband could do so by paying to the father a stipulated amount of cash or cattle for his daughter. This second form of marriage finally evolved into marriage arranged by direct and peaceful negotiation between the prospective husband and wife. This is the form most commonly employed at the present time among the more advanced societies of men. But in the ceremonies which surround the nuptial event among civilised peoples survive vestiges of many of the facts associated with aboriginal marriages. A marriage in high life is a sort of epitome of the evolution of the institution. The coyness and hesitancy of the woman in accepting the offers of her proposed spouse are the lineal descendants of the original reluctance of her savage sisters. The wedding-ring is the old token accepted by the woman when she gave her pledge of bondage. The coming of the groom with his aids to the marriage is a figurative marauding expedition. The honeymoon is the abduction. And the charivari and missile-throwing indulged in by friends and relatives on the departure of the wedded twain is a good-humoured counterfeit of the armed protest made by relatives of old when a bride-snatcher came among them (4).

The vestiges found everywhere in the mental and social phenomena of man and other animals have arisen as necessary facts in the process of mental evolution. *They are the vermiform appendices of the mind.*

8. One of the strongest reasons for a belief in the physical evolution of animal species is that furnished by individual evolution. Each individual animal recapitulates in a wonderful manner the phylogenesis of its species. Now, it is extremely significant that a similar parallel exists in the case of mental evolution. Each individual mind ascends through a series of mental faculties which epitomises in a remarkable manner the psychogenesis of the animal kingdom.

The human child is not born with a full-grown mind any more than with a full-grown body. It grows. It exfoliates. It ripens with the years. It begins in infancy at the zero-point, and in manhood or womanhood may blaze with genius and philanthropy.

But the mind of the child not only unfolds: it unfolds in a certain order, the more complex parts and the more civilised emotions invariably appearing last. The initial powers of the new-born babe are those of sensation and perception. The babe cannot think. It has no feeling of fear, no affection, no sympathy, and no shame. It can see, and hear, and taste, and feel pain and satisfaction—and these are about all. Even these are vague and confused. In a week the perceptions are more sharp and vivid, more distinct and orderly. Memory arises. Memory is the power of reproducing past impressions. At three weeks the emotions begin to sprout. The first to make their appearance are fear and surprise. When the babe is seven weeks old the social affections show themselves, and the simplest acts of association are performed. At the age of twelve weeks jealousy and anger may be expected, together with simple exhibitions of association by similarity. At fourteen weeks affection and reason dawn. Sympathy germinates at about the age of five months; pride and resentment germinate at eight months; grief, hate, and benevolence at ten months; and shame and remorse at fifteen months.

Now, the remarkable thing about this is that this is the order, or very much like the order, in which mind in the animal kingdom as a whole has apparently evolved. The lower orders of animal life have none of the higher emotions and none of the more complicated processes of mind. There is no shame in the reptile, no dissimulation in the fish, no sympathy in the mollusk, and no memory in the sponge. Memory dawns in the echinoderms, or somewhere near the radiate stage of development, and fear and surprise in the worms. Pugnacity makes its appearance in the insects, imagination in the spiders, and jealousy in the fishes. Pride, emulation, and resentment originate in the birds; grief and hate in the carnivora; shame and remorse among dogs and monkeys; and superstition in the savage (1).

It is also an important fact bearing on the general problem of evolution, that the civilised child, from about the age of one on, is a sort of synopsis, rude but unmistakable, of the historic evolution of the human race. The child is a savage. It has the emotions of the savage, the savage's conceptions of the world, and the desires, pastimes, and ambitions of the savage. It hates work, and takes delight in hunting, fishing, fighting, and loafing, like other savages. The hero of the child is the bully, just as the demigod of primitive man is a blood-letting Cæsar or Achilles. The children of the civilised are savages—some more so than others—and if they ever become civilised—some do, and some do not—they do so through a process of rectification and selection similar to that through which the Aryan races have passed during the ages of human history.

There is a similar evolution in the young of other animals, especially of the higher animals. Each individual begins in a perfectly mindless form, and grows mentally as it develops physically. The young puppy has a very different thinking and feeling apparatus from the grown-up mastiff.

It is controlled almost exclusively by sense and instinct. It is devoid of common-sense, and divides its time impartially between play and sleep. It is easily frightened, and cries at every little thing. It has the rollicking, awkward, irresponsible personality of a boy of six. About the same thing is true of kittens, colts, calves, bear cubs, the whelps of wolves, and other young quadrupeds. A kitten will chase shadows, try to catch flies crawling on the other side of a window-pane, sit and watch in wonder the moving objects about it, and do many other things which it never thinks of doing when it has grown to be a wise and sophisticated puss trained in the ways of the world about it. Doghood, cathood, and horsehood, like manhood and womanhood, are the ripened products of long processes of growth and exfoliation.

The parallel is, of course, imperfect. There are many abbreviations, many breaks and ambiguities, in the summary presented by the individual mind of the evolution of the race. And, in the present state of psychogeny, only the barest outline can be traced. *But enough is known to render the fact unquestionable.*

9. If human mind has been evolved, it is logical to expect to find in other animals, especially in those more closely resembling ourselves in structure, mind elements similar to those we find in ourselves.* And this is precisely what we do find.

* This topic is more fully presented in section IV. of this chapter.

The same great trunk impulses that animate men animate also those more rudimentary but not less real individuals below and around men. The great primary facts of sex, of self-preservation, of pleasure and pain, of life and death, of egoism and altruism, of motherhood, of alimentation, etc.— all of these are found everywhere, down almost to the very threshold of organic life. And they are the antecedents of the same great tendencies as those that control the lives of men. It is often supposed by the superficial that the facts of sex and alimentation, which are so prominent in other animals, have been relegated to a very subordinate place in the nature of man. But nothing could be much farther from the truth. It has been said that there are only two things that will induce the typical African or Australian to undergo prolonged labour—hunger and the sex appetite. It is probable that men—not only primitive men, but the most evolved races, including even poets and philosophers—will do more desperate and idiotic things and undergo more trying experiences when actuated by the sex impulse than from the effects of any other impulse in human nature. This impulse is especially overmastering in races like the Italian and Spanish, and has been mentioned by ethnologists as a probable factor in the deterioration of these races. The sentiments of love, marital affection, and family life control mankind more completely than any other motives. And next to these comes hunger. Let anyone who imagines that only the non-human creatures are carnal observe with what uniformity almost every function in both savage and civilised life gravitates toward eating and drinking.   If it is a picnic, a convention, a national holiday, a Christmas celebration, a meeting of a fraternal society, a thanksgiving ceremony, or what not, eating is one of the main things, and the one exercise into which four-fifths of those present probably enter with the greatest enthusiasm.

The human soul is the blossom, not the beginning, of psychic evolution.   Mother - love compassionated infancy long before a babe came from the stricken loins of woman.   The inhabitants of the earth had been seeking pleasure and seeking to avoid pain, and seeking ever with the same sad futility, long before man with his retinue of puny philosophies strutted upon the scene.   Hate poisoned the cisterns of the sea and dropped its pollutions through the steaming spaces ages before there was malice among men.   Altruism is older than the mountains, and selfishness hardened the living heart before the continents were lifted. There was wonder in the woods and in the wild heart of the fastnesses before there were wailings in synagogues and genuflections about altar piles. The frogs, crickets, and birds had been singing love a thousand generations and more when the first amoroso knelt in dulcet descant to a beribboned Venus.   Human nature is not an article of divine manufacture, any more than is the human form. It came out of the breast of the bird, out of the soul of the quadruped.   The human heart does

not draw back from the mysterious dissolutions of
death more earnestly than does the hare that flees
before resounding packs or the wild-fowl that
reddens the reeds with its flounderings. Bower-
birds build their nestside resorts, decorate them
with gay feathers, and surround them with grounds
ornamented with bright stones and shells, for
identically the same reason as human beings
design drawing-rooms, hang them with tapestries,
and surround them with ornamented lawns. The
scarlet waistcoat of the robin and the flaming
dresses of tanagers and humming-birds, which
seem, as they flash through the forest aisles, like
shafts of cardinal-fire, serve the same vanities and
minister to the same instincts as the plumage of
the dandy and the tints and gewgaws of gorgeous
dames. Art is largely a manifestation of sex, and
it is about as old and about as persistent as this
venerable impulse. How did Darwin's dog know
his master on his master's return from a five-years'
trip around the world? Just as the boy remembers
where the strawberries grow and the philosopher
recalls his facts—by that power of the brain to
retain and to reproduce past impressions. Why
does the thinker search his soul for new theories
and the spaces for new stars? For the same
reason that the child asks questions and the
monkey picks to pieces its toys. What is reason?
A habit of wise men—an expedient of ants—a
mania the fools of all ages are free from. All
of the activities of men, however imposing or
peculiar, are but elaborations in one way or

another of the humble doings of the animalcule, whose home is a water-drop and whose existence can be discovered by human senses only by the aid of instruments.

10. Mind has evolved because the universe has evolved. Whether mind is a part of the universe, or all of it, or only an attribute of it, it is, in any case, inextricably mixed up with it. And, since the universe as a whole has evolved, it is improbable that any part of it or anything pertaining to it has remained impassive to the general tendency. There are no solids. Nothing stands. The whole universe is in a state of fluidity. Even the 'eternal hills,' the 'unchanging continents,' and the 'everlasting stars,' are flowing, flowing ever, slowly but ceaselessly, from form to form. So is mind. Indeed, if there is anywhere in the folds of creation a being such as the one whom man has long accused of having brought the universe into existence, we may rest assured that even he is not sitting passively apart from the enormous enterprise which he has himself inaugurated.

The evidence is conclusive. The evolution of mind is supported by a series of facts not less incontrovertible and convincing than that by which physical evolution is established. The data of mental evolution are not quite so definite and plentiful as those of physical evolution. But this is due to the greater intangibility of mental phenomena and to the backward condition of the psychological sciences, especially of comparative psychology. Mental phenomena are always more difficult to deal with than material phenomena, and hence are always more tardily attended to in the application of any theory. But taking everything into account, including the close connection between physical and psychical phenomena, it may be asserted that it is not more certain that the physical structure of man has been derived from sub-human forms of life than it is that the human mind has also been similarly derived.

Man is the adult of long evolution. The human soul has ancestors and consanguinities just as the body has. It is just as reasonable to suppose that the human physiology, with its definitely elaborated tissues, organs, and systems, is unrelated to the physiology of vertebrates in general, and through vertebrate physiology to the physiology of invertebrates, as to suppose that the states and impulses constituting human nature and consciousness began to exist in the anthropic type of anatomy and are unrelated to the states and impulses of vertebrate consciousness in general, and through vertebrate consciousness to those remoter types of sentiency lying away at the threshold of organic life. Human psychology is a part of universal psychology. It has been evolved. It has been evolved according to the same laws of heredity and adaptation as have physiological structures. And it is just as impossible to understand human nature and psychology unaided by those wider prospects of universal psychology as it is to understand the facts of human physiology unaided by analogous universalisations.

III. The Common-sense View.

But it is not necessary to be learned in Darwinian science in order to know that non-human beings have souls. Just the ordinary observation of them in their daily lives about us —in their comings and goings and doings—is sufficient to convince any person of discernment that they are beings with joys and sorrows, desires and capabilities, similar to our own. No human being with a conscientious desire to learn the truth can associate intimately day after day with these people—associate with them as he himself would desire to be associated with in order to be interpreted, without presumption or reserve, in a kind, honest, straightforward, magnanimous manner; make them his friends and really enter into their inmost lives—without realising that they are almost unknown by human beings, that they are constantly and criminally misunderstood, and that they are in reality beings actuated by substantially the same impulses and terrorised by approximately the same experiences as we ourselves. They eat and sleep, seek pleasure and try to avoid pain, cling valorously to life, experience health and disease, get seasick, suffer hunger and thirst, co-operate with each other, build homes, reproduce themselves, love and provide for their children, feeding, defending, and educating them, contend against enemies, contract habits, remember and forget, learn from experience, have friends and favourites and pastimes, appreciate kindness, commit crimes, dream dreams, cry out in distress, are affected by alcohol, opium, strychnine, and other drugs, see, hear, smell, taste, and feel, are industrious, provident and cleanly, have languages, risk their lives for others, manifest ingenuity, individuality, fidelity, affection, gratitude, heroism, sorrow, sexuality, self-control, fear, love, hate, pride, suspicion, jealousy, joy, reason, resentment, selfishness, curiosity, memory, imagination, remorse—all of these things, and scores of others, the same as human beings do.

The anthropoid races have the same emotions and the same ways of expressing those emotions as human beings have. They laugh in joy, whine in distress, shed tears, pout and apologise, and get angry when they are laughed at. They protrude their lips when sulky or pouting, stare with wide-open eyes in astonishment, and look downcast when melancholy or insulted. When they laugh, they draw back the corners of their mouth and expose their teeth, their eyes sparkle, their lower eyelids wrinkle, and they utter chuckling sounds, just as human beings do (5). They have strong sympathy for their sick and wounded, and manifest toward their friends, and especially toward the members of their own family, a devotion scarcely equalled among the lowest races of mankind. They use rude tools, such as clubs and sticks, and resort to cunning and deliberation to accomplish their ends. The orang, when pursued, will throw sticks at his pursuers, and when wounded, and the wound does not prove instantly fatal, will sometimes press his hand upon the wound or apply grass and leaves to stop the flow of blood. The children of anthropoids wrestle with each other, and chase and throw each other, just as do the juveniles of human households. The gorilla, chimpanzee, and orang all build for themselves lodges made of broken boughs and leaves in which to sleep at night. These lodges, rude though they are, are not inferior to the habitations of many primitive men. The Puris, who live naked in the depths of the Brazilian forests, do not even have huts to live in, only screens made by setting up huge palm-leaves against a cross-pole (6). Some of the African tribes are said to live largely in caves and the crevices of rocks. This is the case with many primitive men. According to a writer in the *Journal* of the Anthropological Institute of Great Britain and Ireland (January, 1902), ' common forms of dwelling among the wild tribes of the Malay Peninsula are rock-shelters (sometimes caves, but more commonly natural recesses under overhanging ledges) and leaf-shelters, which are sometimes formed on the ground and sometimes in the branches of trees. The simplest form of these leaf-shelters consists of a single palm-leaf planted in the ground to afford the wanderer some slight shelter for the night.'

When they sleep, the anthropoids sometimes lie stretched out, man-like, on their backs, and sometimes they lie on their side with their hand under their head for a pillow. The orang retires about five or six o'clock in the evening, and does not rise

until the morning sun has dissipated the mists of
the forest.   The gorilla and chimpanzee seem to
mate for life.   The former lives, as a rule, in
single families, each family consisting of a male
and a female and their children.   During the day
this primitive family roams through the forests of
equatorial Africa in search of food.   They live on
fruits and nuts and the tender shoots and leaves
of plants.   They are especially fond of sugar-cane,
which they eat in small-boy fashion by chewing
and discarding the juiceless pulp.   Among the
foods of the gorilla is a walnut-like nut which it
cracks with stones.   As evening comes on, the
head of the family selects a sleeping-place for the
night.   This is usually some low tree with a
dense growth at the top, and protected as much as
possible by higher trees from the chilly night
wind.   Here, on a bed of broken branches and
leaves, the mother and little ones go to sleep,
while the father devotedly crouches at the foot of
the tree, with his back against the trunk to guard
his family from leopards and other nocturnal
cut-throats who eat apes (7).   When the weather
is stormy, they cover themselves with broad
pandanus leaves to keep off the rain.   Koppenfels
relates an incident of a gorilla family which makes
one think of things he sometimes sees among men.
The family consisted of the parents and two
children.   It was meal-time.   The head of the
family reposed majestically on the ground, while
the wife and children hustled for fruits for him
in a near-by tree.   If they were not sufficiently

nimble about it, or if they were so wanton as to take a bite themselves, the paterfamilias growled and gave them a cuff on the head (7). Notwithstanding the sensational tales of the ferocity of this being, the gorilla never attacks anyone at any time unless he is molested (7). He much prefers to attend to his own business. But if he is not allowed to do so, if he is attacked, he is as fearless as a machine. He approaches his antagonist walking upright and beating his breast with his fists. He presents one of the most terrifying of all spectacles, as, with gleaming eyes, hair erect, and resounding yells, he bears down on the object of his resentment. The natives fear the gorilla more than they fear any other animal.

The chimpanzee in his native wilds lives in small tribes consisting of a few families each. Like the gorilla, it passes the most of its time on the ground, going among the trees only for food or sleep. It builds a sleeping-place at night in the trees, as in the case of the gorilla. Brehm, who brought up a number of chimpanzees in his own home as comrades and playmates of his children, and who studied them and associated with them for years, says: 'The chimpanzee is not only one of the cleverest of all creatures, but a being capable of deliberation and judgment. Everything he does is done consciously and deliberately. He looks upon all other animals, except man, as very inferior to himself. He treats children entirely different from grown-up people. The latter he respects; the former he looks upon as comrades and equals. He is not merely inquisitive: he is greedy for knowledge. He can draw conclusions, can reason from one thing to another, and apply the results of experience to new circumstances. He is cunning, even wily, has flashes of humour, indulges in practical jokes, manifests moods, and is entertained in one company and bored in another. He is self-willed but not stubborn, good-natured but not wanting in independence. He expresses his emotions like a human being. In sickness he behaves like one in despair, distorts his face, groans, stamps, and tears his hair. He learns very easily whatever is taught him, as, for instance, to sit upright at table, to eat with knife and fork and spoon, to drink from a glass or cup, to stir the sugar in his tea, to use a napkin, to wear clothes, to sleep in a bed, and so on. Exceedingly appreciative of every caress, he is equally sensitive to blame and unkindness. He is capable of deep gratitude, and he expresses it by shaking hands or kissing without being asked to do so. He behaves toward infants with touching tenderness. The behaviour of a sick and suffering chimpanzee is most pathetic. Begging piteously, almost humanly, he looks into his master's face, receives every attempt to help him with warm thanks, and soon looks upon his physician as a benefactor, holding out his arm to him, stretching out his tongue whenever told, and even doing so of his own accord after a few visits from his physician. He swallows medicines

readily, and even submits to surgical operations—
in short, behaves very like a human patient in
similar circumstances.   As his end approaches,
he becomes more gentle, and the nobler traits of
his character stand out prominently ' (8).

The *New York Herald*, in its issue of July 2,
1901, contained an account of the death of Charle-
magne, a chimpanzee who died a short time before
at Grenoble, France.   This anthropoid at the
time of his death was the most popular inhabitant
of the town.   His popularity was due to his
good-nature and intelligence, and especially to the
fact that a few years before his death he had saved
a child from drowning in a well.   The ape saw
the child fall, and without a moment's hesitation
climbed down the rope used for the buckets, seized
the child, and climbed out again by the same rope
by which he had descended.   The people of the
town thought so much of him that they followed
his remains to the grave, and the municipal council
voted to erect a bronze statue to his memory.

A heartless hunter—maybe one of those assassins
who fill the wilds with widows and orphans in the
name of Science—tells of the murder of a mother
chimpanzee and her baby in Africa.   The mother
was high up in a tree with her little one in her
arms.   She watched intently, and with signs of
the greatest anxiety, the hunter as he moved about
beneath, and when he took aim at her the poor
doomed thing motioned to him with her hand
precisely in the manner of a human being, to have
him desist and go away.

According to Emin Pasha, who was for a number of years Governor of an Egyptian province on the Upper Nile, and whom Stanley made his last expedition to 'rescue,' chimpanzees sometimes make use of fire. He told Stanley that, when a tribe of chimpanzees who resided in a forest near his camp came at night to get fruit from the orchards, they always came bearing torches to light them on their way. 'If I had not seen it with my own eyes,' he declares, 'I never could have believed that these beings have the power of making fire' (9). This same authority relates that on one occasion a band of chimpanzees descended upon his camp and carried off a drum. The marauders went away in great glee, beating the drum as they retreated. He says he heard them several times after that, at night, beating their drum, in the forest.

The monkeys are little inferior to the man-like races in their intelligence and in the general similarity of their feelings and instincts to those of men. Monkeys live in tribes, and at the head of each tribe is an old male chief who has won his place by his strength, courage, and ability. Monkeys have excellent memories and keen observation, and are able to recognise their friends in a crowd even after long absences. They are proverbially imitative, have a strong desire for knowledge, and are exceedingly sensitive and sympathetic in their natures. Sympathy and curiosity, the two most prominent traits in simian psychology, are, significantly, the two most important facts in the psychology of man. Sympathy and curiosity lie at the foundation of human civilisation, sympathy at the foundation of morals, and curiosity of invention and science. The monkey whose diary appears in the closing pages of Romanes' 'Animal Intelligence' was possessed of an almost ravenous desire to know. He spent hour after hour in exploration, examining with the indomitable patience of a scientist everything that came within the bounds of his little horizon. And when he had found out any new thing, he was as delighted over it as a boy who has solved a hard problem, repeating the experiment over and over until it was thoroughly familiar to him. Among the many things he discovered for himself was the use of the lever and the screw. Monkeys are the most affectionate of all animals excepting dogs and men. This affection reaches its culmination, as among men, in the love of the mother for her child. The mother monkey's little one is the object of her constant care and affection. She nurses and bathes it, licks it and cleans its coat, and folds it in her arms and rocks it as if to lull it to sleep, just as human mammas do. She divides every bite with her little one, but does not hesitate to chastise it with slaps and pinches when it is rude. The monkey child is generally very obedient, obedient enough for an example to many a human youngster.

'Very touching,' says Brehm, from whom many of the foregoing facts are gleaned, 'is the conduct of the mother when her baby is obviously suffering. And if it dies she is in despair. For hours, and even for days, she carries the little corpse about with her, refuses all food, sits indifferently in the same spot, and often literally pines to death ' (8).

Orphan monkeys, according to Brehm, are often adopted by the tribe, and carefully looked after by the other monkeys, both male and female. The great mass of human beings, who know about as much about the real emotional life of monkeys as wooden Indians do, are inclined to pass over lightly all displays of feeling by these people of the trees. But the poet knows, and the prophet knows, and the world will one day understand, that in the gentle bosoms of these wild woodland mothers glow the antecedents of the same impulses as those that cast that blessed radiance over the lost paradise of our own sweet childhood. The mother monkey who gathered green leaves as she fled from limb to limb, and frantically stuffed them into the wound of her dying baby in order to stanch the cruel rush of blood from its side, all the while uttering the most pitiful cries and casting reproachful glances at her human enemy, until she fell with her darling in her arms and a bullet in her heart, had in her simian soul just as genuine mother-love, and love just as sacred, as that which burns in the breast of woman.

The affection of monkeys is not confined to the love of the mother for her child, but exists among the different members of the same tribe, and extends even to human beings, especially to those who make any pretensions to do to them as they would themselves be done by. The monkey kept by Romanes, already referred to, became so attached to his master that he went into the wildest demonstrations of joy whenever his master, after an absence, came into the room. Standing on his hind-legs at the full length of his chain, and reaching out both hands as far as he could reach, he screamed with all his might. His joy was so hysterical that it was impossible to carry on any kind of conversation until he had been folded in his master's arms, when he immediately grew quiet.

' After I took this monkey back to the Zoological Gardens,' says Romanes, ' and up to the time of his death, he remembered me as well as the day he was returned. I visited the monkey-house about once a month, and whenever I approached his cage he saw me with astounding quickness— indeed, generally before I saw him—and ran to the bars, through which he thrust both hands with every expression of joy. When I went away he always followed me to the extreme end of the cage, and stood there watching me as long as I remained in sight.'

The following account of the attachment of a male monkey for his murdered consort is a pitiful tale of human inhumanity and of simian tenderness and devotion :

' A member of a shooting-party killed a female monkey, and carried her body to his tent under a banyan-tree. The tent was soon surrounded by forty or fifty of the tribe, who made a great noise and threatened to attack the aggressor. When he presented his fowling-piece, the fearful effects of which they had just witnessed, and appeared perfectly to understand, they retreated. The leader of the troop, however, stood his ground, threatening and chattering furiously. At last, finding threats of no avail, the broken-hearted creature came to the door of the tent and began a lamentable moaning, and by the most expressive signs seemed to beg for the dead body of his beloved. It was given to him. He took it sorrowfully in his arms and bore it away to his expecting companions (10).

The chattering of monkeys is not, as is vulgarly supposed, meaningless vocalisation. It is language. It is meaningless to human ears for the same reason that the chattering of Frenchmen is mean-ingless to Americans—*because human beings are foreigners.* The conversation of monkeys is to convey thought. Every species that thinks and feels has means for conveying its thoughts and feelings, and the means for this exchange, whether it be sounds, symbols, gestures, or grimaces, is language. As Wundt somewhere says : ' If psychologists of to-day, ignoring all that an animal can express through gestures and sounds, limit the possession of language to human beings, such a conclusion is scarcely less absurd than that of many philosophers of antiquity who regarded the languages of barbarous nations as animal cries.' Mr. Garner, who has so long and so sympathetically associated with monkeys, has been able to translate a number of their words and to enter into slight communication with them. Among the words he has been able to understand are the words for 'alarm,' 'good-will,' 'listen,' 'food,' 'drink,' 'monkey,' and 'fruit.' According to him, the simian tongue has about eight or nine sounds which may be changed by modulation into three or four times that number, and each different species or kind has its own peculiar tongue slightly shaded into dialects. There may be more discriminating students than Garner, but few certainly who have approached their favourite problem with more feeling and humanity. Every one should read his beautiful book on 'The Speech of Monkeys.' 'Among the little captives of the simian race,' says he tenderly, in closing his chapter on the emotional character of these people, 'I have many little friends to whom I am attached, and whose devotion to me is as warm and sincere, so far as I can see, as that of any human being. I must confess that I cannot discern in what intrinsic way the love they have for me differs from my own for them; nor can I see in what respect their love is less divine than is my own.'

Dogs are distinguished for their great intelligence, the pre-eminence of the sense of smell, fidelity to duty, nobleness of nature, patience, courage, and affection. In all of these particulars many individual dogs are superior to whole races of men. Dogs are more sensitive to physical suffering than savages, and will cry piteously from slight wounds or other injuries. Dogs of high life have genuine feelings of dignity and self-respect, and are easily wounded in their sensibilities. Such dogs have considerable sense of propriety, and suffer, like sensitive children, from disapprobation. Romanes had a dog that was so sensitive that he resented insult, and so sympathetic that he always fought in defence of other dogs when they were punished or attacked. When out driving with his master, this dog always caught hold of his master's sleeve every time the horse was touched with a whip (10). Romanes also tells of a Scotch terrier who, having grown old and useless, and been supplanted by a younger dog, Jack, became painfully jealous, and imitated his rival in everything that he did, even to ridiculous details, in order to retain the attentions of the household. When Jack was tenderly caressed, the old dog would watch for a time, and then burst out whining as if in the deepest distress (10). Dogs communicate their ideas to each other and to human beings, generally by means of sounds and gestures. They growl in anger, yelp in eagerness, howl in despair, bark in joy or warning, bay in wonder, wail in bitterness and pain, whine in supplication, and prostrate themselves in submission or apology. It has been said that there never was a man who possessed the stateliness of a St. Bernard, the unerring sagacity of the collie, or the courage and tenacity of the bulldog. The vainest dandy is not more delicate in his ways than the Italian greyhound, nor more soft and affectionate than the Blenheim. Many a deed of heroism has been done by dogs which would, if done by men, have been honoured by the Order of the Victoria Cross. The St. Bernards belonging to the monks on the passes between Switzerland and Italy are especially celebrated for their devotion to the business of saving human life. They often lose their own lives in their efforts to rescue travellers baffled and overcome by storm. One particularly sagacious individual, who lost his life in this way some years ago, wore a medal stating that he had been the means of saving twenty-two human lives. In devotion the dog is superior to all other animals, not even excepting man. 'How could one get relief from the endless dissimulation, falsity, and malice of mankind,' exclaimed Schopenhauer in one of his inspired moments, 'if there were no dogs into whose honest faces he could look without distrust?' A dog will follow a handful of rags wrapped around a homeless beggar, day after day, through heat and cold and storm and starvation, just as faithfully as he will follow the purple of a king. The dog who stood over the lifeless body of his master, grieving for recognition and starting at every flutter of his garments, till he himself died of starvation, had in his faithful breast a nobler heart than that which beats in the bosom of most men. And the devotion of Greyfriars Bobby, who every night for twelve years, in all kinds of weather, slept on his master's grave, was well worthy the marble tribute which to-day stands in Edinburgh to his memory. There has never been recorded in the history of the world an instance of more extravagant trust and devotion than that told of the canine companion of a certain vivi-sector, which licked the hand of his master while undergoing the crime of being cut to pieces. Such deeds of self-sacrifice remind one of the tales told of imaginary saints. But they are the deeds of *only dogs*—of beings whom half the world look upon with indifference and contempt, and whom the other half would feel, if they came within reach, under the strictest obligations to kick.

> ' When some proud son of man returns to earth,
> Unknown to glory but upheld by birth,
> The sculptor's art exhausts the pomp of woe,
> And storied urns record who rests below ;
> When all is done, upon the tomb is seen,
> Not what he was, but what he should have been ;
> But the poor dog, in life the firmest friend,
> The first to welcome, foremost to defend,
> Whose honest heart is still his master's own,
> Who labours, fights, lives, breathes, for him alone,
> Unhonoured falls, unnoticed all his worth—
> Denied in heaven the soul he had on earth.'

I am not one of those who regard the evidence for the post-mortem existence of the human soul as being either abundant or conclusive. But of one thing I am positive, and that is, that there are the same grounds precisely for believing in the immortality of the bird and the quadruped as there are for the belief in human immortality. And it is delightful to find great thinkers like Haeckel, great biologists and philosophers, holding the same conviction. Haeckel is the giant of the Germans, and in his brilliant book 'The Riddle of the Universe' appears this rather poetical paragraph : ' I once knew an old head-forester, who, being left a widower and without children at an early age, had lived alone for more than thirty years in a noble forest of East Prussia. His only companions were one or two servants, with whom he exchanged merely a few necessary words, and a great pack of different kinds of dogs, with whom he lived in perfect psychic communion. Through many years of training this keen observer and friend of nature had penetrated deep into the individual souls of his dogs, and he was as convinced of their personal immortality as he was of his own. Some of his most intelligent dogs were, in his impartial estimation, at a higher stage of psychic development than his old stupid maid and his rough and wrinkled man-servant. Any unprejudiced observer who will study the psychic phenomena of a fine dog for a year, and follow attentively the processes of its thought, judgment, and reason, will have to admit that it has just as valid a claim to immortality as man himself.'

Fido was a shaggy terrier who lived years ago in the old home on the farm by the beautiful brook. He was one of the very first acquaintances the writer of these lines made on coming into existence. In his earlier years, before age had dimmed his mind and rheumatism had fastened upon him, he was an exceedingly agreeable and clever canine, active in all the affairs of the farm. He knew the old homestead by heart, and he took about as much interest in having everything go right as anybody—more, perhaps, even than we boys did. He chased the pigs out of the orchard without being asked to do so, and guarded the house at night with the vigilance of a hired watchman. He seemed to realise the demands of everyday situations about as well as any of us. He could distinguish between neighbours who were accustomed to come on the premises and strangers who were not. He always knew when company came, for he invariably attempted to profit by the fact. He had been taught early the propriety of keeping in the background when his tyrants were feeding, and ordinarily on such occasions he slept dutifully by the kitchen stove. But just as sure as a guest sat at table, Fido would turn up, and, tapping the visitor gently to get his attention, would sit up perfectly straight, with his paws pendent and a peculiar grin on his face, in expectation of a morsel. Dear old Fido! How much he thought of all of us! And how meagerly, as I know now, were his matchless love and services requited! On Sundays sometimes the human members of the household would go away and stay all day, and Fido and the cat would be left alone to get along the best way they could. He knew as well as any of us when these days came around, and he dreaded them. I suppose he had learned from experience to associate cessation of farm work and peculiar preparations with a day alone. The long, lonely hours probably affected him somewhat as they do a human being who is compelled to stay alone all day with nothing to do. But what a welcome he gave us in the evening when we came back! This was indubitable evidence of his loneliness. The first familiar object we would see in the evening, on coming in sight of home, was faithful Fido, sitting out in the road on the hill above the house—sitting straight up in that peculiar way of his—watching and waiting for our home-coming. He knew, or seemed to know, the direction from which to expect us, and was able to recognise us a long way off. The years have been many, and Fido's dust has long been scattered by the gusts over the farms of north-west Missouri; but now, in fancy, I can see this faithful creature bounding down the road in the sunset to meet us, as he used to do in the golden long-ago, leaping and smiling and wagging his tail, and wriggling and barking in a perfect ecstasy of gladness.

Well, I *know* Fido could feel and think, that he loved and feared and longed and dreaded and dreamed and hated and grieved and sympathised and reasoned and rejoiced—in short, that he was moved by about the same passions and considerations as human beings usually are. He gave the same evidence of it precisely as a human being does.

The dog is the oldest of human associates. Long before the historical period the dog was domesticated in Europe, Asia, and Africa. No race of men is too primitive to be without the dog. The bones of the dog are found in the middens of the Baltic, and rude representations of it are chiseled on the oldest monuments of Egypt and Assyria. The dog was the servant of man away in paleolithic times, when the mastodon was on earth, and man was a naked troglodyte, and Europe extended westward to the Azores. And he has been a faithful friend, a tireless ally, and an enthusiastic slave of a thankless and inhuman master ever since.

Birds are pre-eminently emotional and artistic. This is shown by their fondness for singing, their fine dress, their pining for their dead, their dainty architecture, their pretty forms and manners of life, their joyousness, and their love for their young. Birds are the most beautiful and engaging of all terrestrial beings. Endowed with the power of flight, eminently active, light-hearted and free, attired in all the colours of the rainbow, and with voices of unrivalled richness and melody, birds are the admiration and envy of all of those that dwell on the earth. Birds possess naturally and in marvellous perfection that power of locomotion which has been so long sought for by slow-shuffling man. Birds are also incomparable musicians, no other animals, not even men, approaching them in the surpassing brilliancy and sweetness of their song. No human musician in high-sounding hall can equal the artless lay of the wild bird ringing melodiously through the leafy colonnades of the woods.

Like men, birds sing chiefly of love; but they also sing for pastime or pleasure. Their singing is sweetest during the season of courtship, and attains its highest development in the males. Birds are ardent lovers. To win their brides, the males contend with each other, and display their charms of plumage and song with the wildness of human Romeos.

The song of birds is generally acquired by inheritance from the species, but is sometimes borrowed by imitation from other birds, or even from other animals. Birds taken from their species when young, before they have heard their native song, sing generally the song of their kind, but it is likely to be interspersed with notes and phrases from the birds around them. Birds thus isolated have been known to adopt entirely the song of their surroundings. Olive Thorne Miller vouches for the fact that an English sparrow she once knew grew up in company with a canary, and came in time to sing the song of its more talented companion to perfection. It must have been a Shakspere of a bird, however, to have soared so high above the excruciating accomplishments of the generality of its species.

The songs of birds can be set to music just as the melodies of men can. The songs of several birds were published in the American *Naturalist* a few years ago. And Winchell, the well-known English student of birds, has written a clever book on the ' Cries and Call-notes of Wild Birds,' in which he prints the calls and songs of most of the native birds of England. According to this writer, who has perhaps studied the music of birds more critically than anyone else, the song of the nightingale, when printed in the notation of ordinary human music, is like a piano solo. It is made up of a score or so of different strains, with trills and crescendos, and all executed in so inimitable a manner that it is unrecognisable when repeated on a musical instrument or the human voice. One of these strains, curiously enough, is identical with the song of a certain bush-warbler of western Canada—as if the English vocalist had plagiarised the song of its humbler cousin in compiling its incomparable repertoire. The song of the mocking-bird is a magnificent medley, made up of the calls, trills, twitters, warbles, warnings, and love-songs, of a score or more of other birds. I have heard this bird along the Solomon and Arkansas valleys repeat in the most perfect manner the notes and songs of the pewee, purple martin, kingbird, flicker, blue jay, catbird, canary, crow, English sparrow, red-headed woodpecker, quail, cardinal, cuckoo, robin, red-wings, grackle, meadow-lark, night-hawk, whip-poor-will, besides many other calls and notes, perhaps of birds I did not know. In the case of some of these birds the mocker made all of the different sounds of each bird. The song of the mocking-bird is delivered at any time, day or night, and generally in a state of high ecstasy and excitement, the performer flying from tree to tree and from house-top to barn-top, occasionally throwing himself into the

air in the most absurd manner, and all the time
pouring forth such a stream of melody that one
would think all the birds in the neighbourhood
had suddenly come together and let loose in a
grand festival of song.

According to Chapman, many of the notes of
birds are language notes rather than sounds expressive of sentiment. Of the robin this well-
known student of birds says: ' The song and
call-notes of this bird, while familiar to everyone,
are in reality understood by no one, and offer
excellent subjects for the student of bird language.
Its notes express interrogation, suspicion, alarm,
and caution, and it signals to its companions to
take wing. Indeed, few of our birds have a more
extended vocabulary.' Winchell says that the
common English sparrow has as many as seven
different notes, which it uses to express the
thoughts and feelings passing through its rather
active but not very highly honoured head: (1) The
common note of address of the male to the female;
(2) a note of alarm used by both male and female
adults, but never by the young; (3) an emphatic
alarm note, always uttered by sentinels when a
hawk is near or when a man approaches with a
gun; (4) the note of the female when surrounded
by several noisy and contending male rivals;
(5) an autumn cry uttered by the first one of the
company perceiving danger and flying up from
the hedges and fields—never uttered by young,
but by adults of both sexes; (6) the love note of
both male and female, used mostly by the female,

and generally with a fluttering or shaking accompaniment of her wings; (7) a curious note sometimes heard in London—meaning not well understood, but supposed to be a sort of chuckle or sign of contentment. Each one of these several different notes may be used to stand for various ideas depending on the circumstances by being given different emphasis and inflection, just as in the languages of many primitive races of men a small vocabulary of words is used to stand for a much larger number of ideas by being pronounced differently. In the Chinese language, for instance, the words are increased to three or four times the original number by modulation; but the same thing is observed in all languages, both human and non-human. Verbal poverty is pieced out by verbal variation. We say *ac'-cent* or *ac-cent'*, depending on whether we wish to express the idea of a noun or a verb.

The memory of birds is well developed. Many of them remember the very grove or meadow, and even the very knot-hole or bush, in which they built their nest the season before, although in the meantime they have journeyed over lands and seas and sojourned thousands of miles away. Every year, for several seasons past, in late summer and early fall, after the nesting-time is over and the young ones are all grown, the purple martins have gathered in large numbers about the Field Columbian Museum, in Jackson Park, Chicago. They stay here for a few weeks, foraging the surrounding air for insects by day, and sleeping on the great dome of the Museum by night, finally flying away to be seen no more in such numbers till next year. These birds, many of them anyway, must remember from one year to another this annual assembly here by the big waters, else why would they come together at this particular spot from all over the country ? I have no doubt that some of them, having sojourned here year after year for some time, remember well the great ugly building where they meet, and are more or less familiar with the surrounding locality from having searched it so often. I wonder what led to the establishing of the custom in the first place. Customs do not fall from the skies. And what advantage is there in the practice ? What are they up to as they chirp and wheel in the air, and flutter up the slopes and sail down again, and perch on the pinnacles and twitter ? Maybe it is a sort of Saratoga for them, where they all come together ostensibly to dip their bills in the blue waves, but where sons swell in their new feathers, and sly mammas find prospects for unmarketable misses.

A parrot has been known to remember the voice of its mistress after an absence of a year and a half—a very remarkable feat even for the grey matter of a bird. A flock of geese mentioned by Romanes showed their knowledge of the arrival of market-day, which came every two weeks, by assembling regularly on such days, early in the morning, in front of the town inn where the market was held, to pick up the corn. They never came on the wrong day; and on one occasion, when the market was omitted on account of a holiday, here came the unfailing fowls cackling and shouting as usual in merry anticipation of their fortnightly feast, but ignorant of the national necessities which had doomed them to be disappointed (10).

Parrots remember and call for their absent friends, and mumble phrases in their dreams which have been taught to them. These gifted birds learn long poems by heart, and sing songs with considerable art. A parrot belonging to the canon of the Cathedral of Salzburg was given instruction regularly two hours every day for ten years, from 1830 to 1840. The bird became very proficient in speech and exceedingly intelligent. It took part in conversations, whistled tunes, and was able to sing a number of popular songs, among them an entire aria from Flotow's opera of 'Martha' (11).

Educated birds though, like educated dogs, horses, cats, mice, men, and everything else, are very different beings from the uneducated. Cultivation is a key that unlocks all sorts of miracles. Cats are cultivated tigers; and the richest grains that ripen in the fields of men, and the loveliest flowers that blow, are only educated weeds. Even the flea may be taught to exchange leaping for walking, to draw a tiny wagon, to ride on the seat, to fire a toy cannon, and do many other feats.

There is one family of birds in which the

superior size, gorgeousness, and vivacity, usual to the males, are found in the other sex, the females being the larger and more brightly coloured—the Phalarope family. Indeed, the members of this small family not only reverse the usual arrangement of the sexual characters of birds, but completely upset many of the most cherished traditions of the avian household. The female does the wooing, and takes the lead in selecting the nest site. And while she lays the eggs, the privilege of incubation she hands over magnanimously to her dull-coloured mate.

Birds have a keen observation and a good deal of that invaluable faculty known as common-sense. It is wonderful how quickly they learn to avoid telegraph-wires when these invisible but deadly gossamers are first stretched across a country, and how unerringly they keep at safe distances when hunted with firearms. An experienced crow can tell a cane from a gun-barrel almost as far as he can see it.

Nearly all birds build nests of some kind in which to cradle their eggs and young. The cow-bird and cuckoo (European), however, are exceptions. These birds have the rather human practice of turning their cares and labours over to somebody else. They are loafers and parasites. They lay their eggs secretly in the nests of other birds, where their eggs are hatched and their young cared for by an alien mother. I have seen a mother song-sparrow hustling about among the shrubs and grasses for an hour at a time almost, gathering food for a young cow-bird nearly twice as big as she was, while her foundling sat phlegmatically at the foot of a tree chirping and fluttering its wings, and acting as a thankless and apparently bottomless receptacle for the morsel after morsel laboriously harvested for it by its tireless little foster-mother.   Sand-martins and kingfishers burrow in the earth and rear their broods in subterranean cradles; gulls and game-birds build on the ground; the flamingoes and barn-swallows build mud nests; the woodpeckers mine holes in trees; doves and eagles make platforms of sticks; the tailor-bird bastes living leaves together; the social weavers construct great straw roofs covering the top of a tree, and build their nests on the limbs beneath; most singing birds build daintily-lined baskets, and swing them in trees and bushes.

It is often said that all the birds of a species build their nests in precisely the same way, and that, while men change and improve their dwelling-places from generation to generation, birds build their abodes in the same old way, just as their ancestors built theirs centuries and centuries ago. This is a favourite thought with the fogies, with those who change not in their thinking from the ways hacked out for them centuries and centuries ago.   Birds are like men.   Some of them—some races and some individuals—are much more given to initiative than others.   There is as wide a difference between the hang-bird and the auk in the construction of their domiciles as between the millionaire and the savage. And the hang-bird has come by her home-making art through centuries of improvement, just as the millionaire has arrived at his. It is believed by ornithologists that the first nests of birds were the niches of rocks or simple hollows scooped in the sand and soil, such as are still seen among the more primitive bird races, and that from these aboriginal beginnings have come, through ages of evolution, the elaborate creations of the cotton-bird, weaver-bird, tailor-bird, oven-bird, the baya-sparrow, the finches, and the orioles. The savage who lives unmolested generation after generation in the same land and country builds his simple hut in just the same way as his ancestors built theirs, and thinks the same things his ancestors thought a thousand years before him. Sir Samuel Baker, in a paper on ' The Races of the Nile Basin,' points out that each tribe of men in eastern Africa, like each species of bird, has its own peculiar style of hut, and that the huts of the various tribes are as constant in their types as are the nests of birds. The same thing is true of their head-dresses as of their huts ; and this fixed character exists also in their languages, customs, and re-ligions. It is only *some* races of men that are given to growth and fluidity, and only *some men* of these special races.

Right in our own country, among the remote mountain recesses of Appalachia, surrounded on all sides by the most wonderful development, material and intellectual, the world has ever seen,

lives a race of rude mountain folk almost as
aboriginal in their ways and views of life, and as
unaffected by civilisation, as if they were in the
heart of Africa. They live huddled together in
one-room log-cabins without windows or floors,
eat bacon and cornmeal, carry on almost constant
wars, and execute the deputies of civilisation who
happen to stray into their illicit dominions, just
as they have done from the time these mountain
silences were first broken by them 150 or 200
years ago.

Birds, as a rule, use a great deal of care and
thought in the location of their nests. After they
have selected a certain grove or field as the one
best suited to their purposes, or as the one around
which cluster the happiest memories, it usually
requires several days of flying and peeping about,
of spying and exploration, before the exact spot
for the precious domicile is finally settled upon.
It is a delicate matter for many birds, for security
from sun, storm, and enemies must all be taken
into account. Old birds, as has been frequently
observed, build better nests and select more clever
locations for their nests than the young and
inexperienced. The nest-building habits of many
birds are known to have changed during the past
few hundred years. The American house-swallow
did most certainly not build under the eaves of
human houses 300 years ago, nor did the hair-bird
ine her nest with horsehair as she invariably
does now. The fact that wrens, swifts, and
martins now build almost altogether in boxes and

chimneys shows that birds are able and willing to adapt themselves to new conditions. The chimney-swift and purple martin, it is said, still cling to their aboriginal custom of rearing their young in hollow trees in the unsettled parts of America. The indomitable house-sparrow builds its nest almost anywhere, from knot-holes and tin cans to electric-light globes and tree-tops. Its original dwelling was probably an arboreal affair, like that of other sparrows, and different nesting-places have been adopted as a result of its association with man. Not only in its architecture, but in several other ways, this bird has departed from the traditions of its tribe. The Fringillidæ (the sparrow family of birds) are seed-eaters, both in structure and practice. But the house-sparrow, since it left the fields and groves to become a gamin on human streets, has learned to eat almost anything, and one thing, too, about as cheerfully as another. The varied habits of this bird are probably due to its natural elasticity in the first place, supple-mented by the unsettling influences of its rather kaleidoscopic experiences during the past few hundred years.

The fear of birds for man is an acquired trait due to ages of persecution. If man would treat birds kindly, they would act toward him as they do toward any other friendly animal. When unfrequented islands are first visited by man, the birds are found to be perfectly fearless of him, flying about him, feeding from his hand, and manifesting no more timidity than if he were a big-hearted bird himself. Darwin states that, when he stopped at the Galapagos Islands on his famous trip around the world in the *Beagle*, he found the birds there so tame that he could push them from the branches of the trees with his gun-barrel. Professor Cutting, of the State University of Iowa, in an article in the *Popular Science Monthly* for August, 1903, tells of the almost absolute fearlessness of the birds on the island of Laysan, an isolated atoll in the Pacific west of the Hawaian Islands, which he visited during that summer. The island swarms with bird life—petrels, alba-trosses, and tropical birds of various kinds—and these birds betray no more fear in the presence of man than if he were a cow. The albatrosses were so numerous and so indifferent to the presence of man that it was necessary to shove them aside with one's foot to keep from stepping on them when one went for a walk along the sand-stretches of the shore. Professor Cutting took photographs of birds which literally posed for him in all sorts of positions, and half-savage jackies amused them-selves by going about and pulling the pretty tail feathers from the tropical birds as they sat on their nests. I have known of two cases where persons, by going to the same place day after day with food and kindness, have in the course of a few weeks taught robins, sparrows, and other birds, to lose all fear of them, so much so as to sit on their shoulders and arms and eat out of their hands. This is the spirit all birds would show all the time toward their featherless lords if these featherless ones would only treat them with half the consideration they merit.

The love of a bird for the treasures of her nest is one of the most beautiful things of this world. Mother-like, the parent bird will do anything almost for the sake of her little ones. Who has not seen the kildeer strive with all the tact of her clever little soul to allure some big giant of a human being, who has wandered into her neighbourhood, away from her nest of precious young? Many a time as a boy on the farm I have followed one of these birds limping and tumbling and fluttering along on the ground a few feet ahead of me, utterly disabled, as I supposed, but always managing to keep just a little beyond the reach of my eager hands. And when the artful mother has led me far from the sacred spot where lay all there was in this world to her, how triumphantly she has lifted herself on her unharmed wings and, to my utter astonishment, sailed away. The partridge and the mourning-dove are, if possible, even more artful in their acting than the kildeer. After I became a large boy and had been told the meaning of these exhibitions by parent birds, I often followed the mourning-dove, thinking the bird must be really wounded after all, so perfectly did it pretend. But the cunning of the kildeer is not confined to luring one away from the nest. If by some accident one finds her nest (and the nest is so cleverly concealed that, if it is discovered at all, it will be by pure accident), the resourceful mother is ready with other expedients to outwit you. She watches you all the time from the proper distance, and knows by your conduct the moment you have found her nest. And before you have even had time to admire the skill displayed by the mother in blending so perfectly her abode with its surroundings, a single peculiar note from her has caused the whole nestful of cuddling young ones to dart out of their cradle and disappear among the surrounding clods as if by magic. No amount of searching can find one of them. They have vanished as effectually as if they had evaporated. And it is enough to touch the heart of the most indifferent to see the anxious mother bird, as I have seen her from the cranny of a neighbouring rock-pile, come back to her nest and call her scattered children together again after they have once dispersed at her command. Circling around the nest two or three times to assure herself that no one is nigh, she alights and begins a low clucking sound like that of a hen calling her brood. The little ones come out of their hiding-places one after another as mysteriously as they vanished. You can't see for the life of you where they come from. They seem to just *emanate*. And if one of them fails to come at her call—for the devoted mother knows very well just how many she has—she extends her search farther out from her nest, looking all around and keeping up that peculiar little cluck, until the half-scared-to-death little slyboots finally comes creeping out from his improvised snuggery somewhere. If a kildeer's nest has once been found, and the mother feels that it is in danger of future visits, she will move her family at night to some other locality, and it is practically impossible ever to find it again. The family relations of the ring-dotterels are said to be 'so charming and touching that even hunters recoil from shooting a female surrounded by her young ones.'

Human beings, true to their instinct never to call into action their ability to think if they can employ their faculty for nonsense instead, call this love of the mother bird 'machinery.' But there are some of us (and our numbers are increasing) who are disposed to put off the adoption of this conclusion until we go mad. The bird builds her nest, weaving it of the rarest fibres. She hides it in the copse or prudently hangs it far out on some inaccessible bough. She lays her beautiful eggs, and hatches them with the warmth and life of her own breast. She tends her young, bringing them food and drink, and watching over them with a tender and tireless vigilance. She protects them in storm with her own little body, worries about them when danger lurks, and dreams of them, no doubt, as she rocks and sleeps under the silent stars. She sings to them in the overflow of her gladness and hope, and risks her very existence to shield them from harm. She teaches them to fly, to find their food, and to detect their enemies. She is true to her mate, and her mate is true and kind to her. As the days of summer shorten, and the cool, long nights warn of approaching autumn, she leads her children away from the old place, she and her faithful mate, out into the wide old world. And I say there is love in the heart of that mother as truly as in the heart of woman, and there are joy and genuineness and sorrow and fidelity in that sylvan home more sacred than may sometimes bloom in the cold mansions of men.

Conjugal love is also very strong in many of the feathered races, especially among those in which the wedding is for successive seasons or for life. The pining of love-birds for their dead sweethearts is well known. The mandarin duck is proverbial for its marital faithfulness, and a pair of these fowls is carried by the Chinese in their marriage processions as an emblem of constancy. Many instances are recorded of birds, after having been deprived of their mates, refusing steadfastly the attentions of other birds, and even sometimes separating themselves entirely from the society of their kind. The following account of the devotion of a widowed pigeon for her deceased consort sounds like a tale of human woe :

'A man set to watch a field much patronised by pigeons shot an old male pigeon who had long been an inhabitant of the farm. His mate, around whom he had for many a year cooed, whom he had nourished with his own crop and had assisted in rearing numerous young ones, immediately settled on the ground by his side. She refused to leave him, and manifested her grief in the most expressive manner. The labourer took up the dead bird and hung it on a stake. The widow still refused to forsake her husband, and continued day after day slowly walking around the stake on which his body hung. The kind-hearted wife of the farmer heard of the matter, and went to the relief of the stricken bird. On arriving at the spot, she found the poor bird still watching at the side of her dead, and making an occasional effort to get to him. She was much spent with her long fasting and grief. She had made a circular beaten path around the corpse of her companion ' (12).

And these are the beings whose bones men jest over at their feasts, and brutes shoot for pastime on human holidays. Much has been said of the sorrow of birds for their deceased mates, but not too much. For the avian soul may be smothered by the gloom and loneliness that come upon the heart, when the great light of love and companionship has gone out, quite as completely as the soul of a bereaved human. In not many human homes where loved ones lie sick and dying are felt the pangs of more genuine grief than those sometimes suffered by birds when their friends and companions are stricken in death. The following incident, vouched for by Dr. Franklin, who observed it, is only one among many such instances recorded in the literature on birds :

A pair of parrots had lived together on the most loving terms for four years, when the female was taken with a serious attack of gout. She grew rapidly worse, and was soon so weak as to be unable to leave her perch for food, when the male, faithful and tender as a human spouse, took it upon himself to carry food to her regularly in his beak. ' He continued feeding her in this way for four months, but the infirmities of his companion increased day by day, until at last she was no longer able to support herself on the perch. She remained cowering down in the bottom of the cage, making from time to time ineffectual efforts to regain her perch. The male was always near her, and did everything in his power to aid the feeble efforts of his dear better-half. Seizing the poor invalid by the beak or the upper part of her wing, he tried his best to enable her to rise, and repeated his efforts several times. His constancy, his gestures, and his continued solicitude, all showed in this affectionate bird the most ardent desire to relieve the sufferings and assist the weakness of his sinking companion. But the scene became still more affecting when the female was dying. Her unhappy consort moved about her incessantly, his attentions and tender cares redoubled. He even tried to open her beak to give some nourishment. He ran to her, and then returned with a troubled and agitated look. At intervals he uttered the most plaintive cries; then, with his eyes fixed on her, kept a mournful silence. At length his companion breathed her last. From that moment he pined away, and in the course of a few weeks died ' (10).

Even the rough-looking ostrich has sensibility enough to die of a broken heart, as was the case in the Jardin des Plantes at Paris a few years ago.

There is many a heart with a slabless grave far from the haunts of men, and many a tear in secret brews that never wets the eye.

The individual who has never acquired the enthusiasm for a knowledge of the birds and a love for their presence and association has omitted some of the richest emotions of life. ' The sight of a bird or the sound of its voice is at all times an event of such significance to me,' says Chapman, 'a source of such unfailing pleasure, that when I go afield with those to whom birds are strangers I am deeply impressed by the comparative barrenness of their world, for they live in ignorance of a great store of enjoyment that might be theirs for the asking.'

> ' I cannot love the man who does not love,
> As men love light, the song of happy birds.'

I have seen a mother mouse in a moment of peril flee from her home among the falling pieces of a cord-wood pile, and disappear under the roots of a neighbouring oak. I have seen her a little later, recovered from her initial dismay, making her way back again, clambering along among the tangled timbers, stopping now and then to look and listen, her eyes wild and anxious, and her whole little body quaking with excitement. I have seen her go among the ruins of her dwelling, take a poor little squeaking young one in her mouth, and hurry away with it to the gloomy refuge in the roots of the oak. I have watched her return again and again, each time taking in her careful teeth the tiny body of a babe, until five mouthfuls of precious pink were safely lodged within the fortress of the oak. And I could as soon believe that woman, when she saves her children from some fearful harm, is a soulless machine as think that that brave little wood-mother, out there alone under the trees, snatching her darlings from the jaws of death, was a heroine without sense or feeling. That little hairy mother with four feet and bead-like eyes loved her young ones in just the same way and for just the same reason as a human mother loves her young ones. She looked upon her babies, in all probability, with the same mother-love and tenderness as a human mother looks upon hers, and felt in miniature, with evil hovering above them, the same consternation a woman feels when destruction reaches out after those that are nearest and dearest. And when it was all over, when the good angel of deliverance had finally spread its healing white wings over that afflicted family, the heart of that little rodent was doubtless soothed by the same joy as that which, in the hour of deliverance, calms the hearts of humankind.

Ants tend their fields, gather their harvests, domesticate other insects, and keep slaves. They help each other bear heavy burdens, extricate each other from misfortune, speak to each other when they meet, and bury their dead. They build roads and bridges, and manifest wonderful engineering skill in their construction. They even tunnel under rivers. They go far from home, and find their way back again. They inhabit towns, and build splendid and spacious palaces. Each ant knows every other citizen of its own town, and an ant from any other town is immediately recognised as a foreigner. Ants have their overseers of industrial enterprises, and regular hours for work and sleep. The ant is the most pugnacious of all animals, and the most muscular compared with its size. It will boldly attack the biggest creature that walks if this creature invades its home. It will fasten its mandibles into an enemy, and allow itself to be torn to pieces without relaxing its hold. Among some savage tribes, certain species of ants are said to be used as surgeons. Infuriated ants are allowed to fasten their mandibles on the opposite edges of a gash, and in this way the wound is closed. The ants are decapitated, and their bodiless heads with their relentless jaws serve as stitches to the wound. Ants have holidays and athletic festivals. On such occasions they romp and chase each other and play hide-and-seek like children. They stand on their hind-legs, embrace each other with their fore-limbs, grasp each other by the feet or antennæ, pull each other down the entrances to their towns, wrestle and roll over on the sand, and so on—all in the friendliest manner. It is greatly to the credit of these little people that no observer has ever yet known them to become so inventively helpless or so athletically hard up as to play slug-ball. Ants educate their young, and practise the fundamental principles of human states and societies. Forel, the great Swiss student

of ants, says that several hundred nests are sometimes united into a single confederation.   Each
ant knows every other ant of the entire confederation, and they all take part in the common
defence.   Haeckel says, speaking of social evolution in ants, that the aboriginal ants of the Chalk
Age had as little idea of the division of labour and
organisation of modern ant states as paleolithic
flint-chippers had of the complexity and organisation of twentieth-century civilisation.   'If we take
an ant's nest, we not only see that work of every
description—rearing of progeny, foraging, building, rearing of aphides, and so on—is performed
according to the principles of voluntary mutual
aid, but we must also recognise, with Forel, that
the fundamental feature of the life of many species
of ants is the obligation of every ant to share its
food, already swallowed and partly digested, with
every member of the community which may apply
for it.   Two ants belonging to the same nest or
to the same confederation of nests will approach
each other, exchange a few movements with the
antennæ, and if one of them is hungry or thirsty
—and especially if the other has its crop full—it
immediately asks for food.   The individual thus
requested never refuses.   It sets apart its mandibles, takes a proper position, and regurgitates a
drop of transparent fluid, which is licked up by
the hungry ant.   Regurgitating food for others is
so prominent a feature in the life of the ants, and
it so constantly recurs both for feeding hungry
comrades and for feeding larvæ, that Forel con-

siders the digestive tube of ants to consist of two different parts, one of which—the posterior—is for the special use of the individual, and the other— the anterior part—is chiefly for the use of the community. If an ant which has its crop full has been selfish enough to refuse to feed a comrade, it will be treated as an enemy. If the refusal has been made while its kinsfolks were fighting with some other species, they will fall upon the greedy individual with greater vehemence even than upon the enemies themselves. All this has been confirmed by the most accurate observations and experiments' (20).

Ants keep slaves. And the slaves, in some instances, carry their masters about, feed them, groom them, and attend to their every want, just as human lackeys do helpless aristocrats. In some species the institution of slavery is so old that the physical structures of the masters have been modified until the masters are physically unable to feed themselves, and will perish from hunger, though surrounded by food, if they are left to themselves. The brain of the ant, as Darwin says, is one of the most wonderful bits of matter in the universe. It is scarcely one-fourth the size of the head of a pin, yet it is the seat of the most astonishing wisdom and activity. If human intelligence were as great, compared with the mass of the human brain, as is the ant's, man would be several hundred times as wise as he is now, and would then probably not fall far short of that state of erudition which the average man

imagines he already represents.   Ants remember,
and a fact becomes impressed by repetition, showing that the faculty of memory in ants is governed
by the same laws as is this faculty in man.   Sir
John Lubbock found it necessary to *teach* his ants
the way by repeating the lesson where the way
was long or unusual.   'Sensation, perception, and
association follow in the social insects, on the
whole, the same fundamental laws as in the vertebrates, including ourselves.   Furthermore, attention is surprisingly developed in insects' (Forel).
Ants keep standing armies, make alliances, and
maraud neighbouring states.   They have their
wars, civil and foreign, and their massacres and
enslavements of the conquered.   But they have
never got so low yet, so far as anyone knows, as
to hypocritically prosecute their conquests in the
name of God and humanity.   The battlefields of
ants resemble the carnage-plains of men, strewn
with ghastly corpses and covered with the headless and dying.   And the accounts of their expeditions—their going forth in regular columns, with
captains, scouts, and skirmish lines, their battles,
and their return laden with plunder and captives
—read like the grisly tales of human history.
Ants perform, in short, about all the antics of
civilised man, except maltreating the females and
drinking gin.   And shall we say their civilisation
is less real because it is miniature and because it
is carried on far below the Brobdingnagian con-
templations of man ?   'When we see an ant-hill
tenanted by thousands of industrious inhabitants,

excavating chambers, forming tunnels, making roads, guarding their home, gathering food, feeding the young, tending their domestic animals, each one fulfilling its duties industriously and without confusion, it is difficult altogether to deny them the gift of reason or to escape the conviction that their mental powers differ from those of men not so much in kind as in degree ' (Lubbock).

The industrious and gifted bee, with its wonderful social system, in advance even of that of the most enlightened societies of men ; the generous horse, who thinks and feels so much more than the clowns who maul him ever suspect ; the artful spider, that confirmed waylayer lurking in his lair of silk ; the soft and predaceous cat ; the timid-hearted hare, poor hounded little dweller of the fields and stream-sides ; the beautiful and vivacious squirrel ; the lowly lady-bug ; the cautious fox ; the irascible serpent, so cruelly misunderstood by men ; the patient camel ; the scornful peafowl ; the indomitable goat ; the grave and vindictive elephant ; the ingenious beaver, the woodman of the primeval wilderness ; the lordly and polygamous cock ; the maternal hen ; the wary trout, beset everywhere by the villainous traps of impostors ; the bride-like butterfly ; the delicate antelope and deer ; and the sturdy, incorruptible ox—all of these beings have within them souls composed primarily of the same elements as those that compose the souls of men.

Ground-wasps have been observed to use tiny stones as hammers in packing the dirt firmly over their nests—a very remarkable act of intelligence, since the use of tools is not common even among the higher mammals (13). Fishes have been taught to assemble at the ringing of a bell, and toads and tortoises to come at the call of their favourite friends. An alligator which was kept tame for several years became so much attached to its master that 'it followed him about the house like a dog, scrambling up the stairs after him, and showing much affection and docility.' The favourite friend and companion of this alligator was the cat ; and, whenever the cat stretched herself on the floor in front of the fire, the alligator would lie down beside her, with its head on the cat, and go to sleep. 'When the cat was absent, the alligator was restless, but it always appeared happy when the cat was near it' (12).

Wolves and foxes sometimes cooperate with each other in their hunting expeditions, somewhat as men do in theirs. One of their number will crouch in ambush by the side of a road known to be used by hares or other small animals, and leap on the unsuspecting fugitives when driven that way by others of the hunting band. Many animals post sentinels when they eat or sleep or engage in other hazardous undertakings, and these sentinels show a good deal of discrimination in distinguishing between animals that are friendly and those that are not. Beavers not only build lodges to live in, but also construct dams to keep the water in which the villages are located at a certain height. The outlet of these dams is carefully regulated, being regularly lessened and enlarged to suit the supply of water in the stream. The trees used by the beavers in their enterprises are felled by them along the margins of the stream, and floated to the place where they are used. In old communities, where the supply of timber near the stream has been exhausted, artificial canals are cut by these indomitable engineers for use in the transportation of their materials. These excavations are made at a great cost of labour and for the deliberate purpose of enabling the builders to accomplish that which they could not accomplish in any other way. ' In executing this purpose,' says Romanes, 'there is sometimes displayed a depth of engineering forethought over details of structure required by the circumstances of special localities which is even more astonishing than the execution of the general idea' (10). When, for instance, a canal has been carried so far from the original water-supply that, owing to the rising ground, it cannot be continued without a very great expenditure of effort in digging, a second dam is built higher up-stream, and with water drawn from this the canal is continued on at a higher level. Sometimes a third dam is built above the second, and the canal again continued at a still higher level before the valuable timber of the higher grounds is reached. These enterprising rodents also carve sometimes enormous channels across the necks of land formed by winding rivers, to serve as cut-offs in travel and transportation.

And yet all of these things—all of the intelligence, feeling, and ingenuity displayed by the non-human races—are still lumped together by belated psychologists under the head of 'instinct,' by which is meant a blind, unconscious knack of doing the right thing without in any way realising what is being done or what it is being done for! The principle in accordance with which mind is denied to non-human beings would, if carried to its legitimate conclusions, make machines out of all of us, and limit the possession of conscious intelligence to the individual who promulgates the theory. The attitude assumed by many psychologists toward the mental faculties of inferior races reminds one of Heine's interview with the old lizard at Lucca. In the discussion which ensued between the poet and the reptile, the poet dropped the words, ' I think.' ' Think !' snapped the lizard with a sharp, aristocratic tone of profound contempt—'think! Which of you thinks? For 3,000 years, wise sir, I have investigated the spiritual functions of animals, and I have made men and apes the special objects of my study. I have devoted myself to these queer creatures with as great zeal and diligence as Lyonnet to his caterpillars. And as the result of my researches, I can assure you no man thinks. Now and then something occurs to him, and these accidentally occurring somethings he calls thoughts, and the stringing of them together he calls thinking. But you can take my word for it, no man thinks—no philosopher thinks. And, so far as philosophy is concerned, it is mere air and water, like pure vapours in the sky. There is, in reality, only one true philosophy, and that is engraven in eternal hieroglyphics on my own tail' (11).

This attitude of the lordly saurian toward the human race is a stinging burlesque on the anthropocentric conceit which perverts all of man's views of the other orders of life.

It is not contended that non-human beings are psychically identical with human beings. The races of men are not psychically identical with each other. The difference between the intellectual splendours of a Spencer evolving volumes of the profoundest philosophy and the mind of an Australian who cannot count six, or between the understanding of an Edison, the wizard of the electrical world, and that of the South Sea islanders, who, when Captain Cook gave them some English nails, planted them in the hope of raising a new crop, is almost infinite. The lowest races of men have neither superstition nor the power of abstract thought as have the higher races. They have a word for black stone, white stone, and brown stone, but no word for stone; for elm-tree, oak-tree, and the like, but no word for tree. As Kingsley says, 'It is difficult to believe that a dog does not form as clear an abstract idea of a tree as these people do.' There are human beings living in the forests of Asia, Africa, and Australasia that wander about from place to place in herds without chief, law, weapons, or fixed habitations. They go naked, mate by chance, and climb trees like monkeys. Some of these races know nothing of fire, religion, or a moral world, chatter to each other like apes, and live on such natural products as roots, fruits, serpents, mice, ants, and honey. One of these creatures, we are told, will lie flat on his front for an hour by the runway of a field-mouse, waiting for a chance to snatch up the little creature when it comes along and eat it. Dozens of such degraded races are mentioned by Büchner in his 'Man: Past, Present, and Future,' and by Sir John Lubbock in his 'Origin of Civilisation.'

Non-human beings have, as a rule, neither the psychic variety nor the intensity of higher humans. And it is not contended that in language, science, and superstition they are capable of being compared with the foremost few of civilised societies, any more than savages, especially the lowest savages, are capable of such comparison. But it *is* maintained that the non-human races of the earth are *not* the metallic and soulless lot of fixtures they are vulgarly supposed to be; that they are just as real living beings, with just as precious nerves and just as genuine feelings, rights, heartaches, capabilities, and waywardnesses, as we ourselves; and that, since they are our own kith and kindred, we have no right whatever, higher than the right of main strength (which is the right of devils), to assume them to be, and to treat them as if they were, our natural and legitimate prey.

IV. The Elements of Human and Non-human Mind Compared.

The analysis of human mind and the comparison of its elements or powers with the powers of non-human mind corroborate the conclusions already arrived at through observation and deductive inference. The chief powers of the mind of man are *sensation, memory, emotion, imagination, volition, instinct,* and *reason.* All of these faculties are found in non-human beings, some of them developed to a much higher degree than they are in man, and some of them to a much lower.

Sensation is the effect produced on the mind when a sense organ is affected in some way by external stimuli. Sensation is the lumber of the mind, the raw material out of which are elaborated all other forms of consciousness. The chief species of sensation are those of sight, sound, smell, taste, and feeling. The original sense was feeling, and out of this sense were evolved the other four. The organs of seeing, hearing, smelling, and tasting are therefore modifications of the skin, which is the organ of original sense. The fact that in all animals, down almost to the very beginnings of life, sense organs exist, suggests that sensation may be almost, if not quite, coextensive with animal life. All mammals, birds, reptiles, amphibians, and fishes have the same special sense organs as man, and the organs of sight, sound, taste, and smell occupy in all vertebrates the same relative positions in the head. Birds see better than any other animals, and carnivora smell better. Ruminants see, hear, and smell with great acuteness. Fishes also see and hear well; and the wings of the bat are so exceedingly sensitive that it will move about blindfolded and with ears stopped with cotton almost as unerringly as when aided by sight and sound. Insects have smell, sight, and taste well developed, as is shown by their keen appreciation of the colours, perfumes, and flavours of flowers. They also hear. Stridulation proves this. Worms have eyes and ears, and land-leeches scent the approach of their prey at a long distance. The starfish and the medusa respond to all the five classes of stimuli which affect the five senses of man, and nervous substance is found in all animals above the sponge.

Memory is the power of retaining or recognising past states of consciousness. The power to retain impressions follows in origin close upon the power to receive impressions. Memory is the historic faculty of the mind—the power of the mind to store up its experiences—and is found in nearly all animals. The lowly limpet, whose world is a seaside rock, will come back from its little roamings time after time to the same rude lodge from which it set out. Bees remember where they get honey or sugar months afterwards, and when it is necessary will sometimes go back to the old home hive which they left the year before. Ants retrace their steps after making long journeys from their nest, and are able in some way to recognise their friends after months of separation. The stickleback (fish) knows the way back to his nest, although he has been absent several hours. Fishes return and hatch their young year after year in the same waters; birds come back to their old nesting-places; and horses remember their way along devious roads over which they have not been for years. Horses used in the delivery of milk, or in other occupations in which they are accustomed to travel daily over about the same route, come in time to remember every alley, street, and stopping-place of the whole round almost as accurately as their drivers. Darwin's dog remembered and obeyed him after an absence of five years. The power of dogs, squirrels, and other animals of remembering where they have long before câched food is indeed wonderful. A squirrel will come down out of a tree when the earth is covered to a depth of several inches with lately fallen snow and hop away, without the slightest hesitancy or mistake, to the exact spot where it has months before stored its mid-winter acorns. · A lion has been known to recognise its keeper after seven years of separation, and an elephant obeyed all his old words of command on being recaptured after fifteen years of jungle life. The similarity of memory in other animals to the same faculty in man is shown by the fact that memory everywhere is governed by the same laws. In all animals, including man, memory is strengthened by repe-tition—that is, impressions are always deepened and confirmed by being made over and over. A parrot or a raven masters a new sentence by working at it and saying it over and over again, just as a boy memorises his rules and catechisms.

Imagination is the picturing power of the mind. In its lowest stages of manifestation it is akin to memory. Imagination, however, in its higher reaches, not only reimages previous impressions, but combines them in new and original relations. Imagination is displayed in dreams, images, delusions, anticipation, and sympathy. It also furnishes wings for speculation and reason. Spiders, when they attach stones to their webs to steady them during anticipated gales, probably exercise imagination. The tame serpent which was carried away from its master's house and found its way back again, though the distance was one hundred miles, no doubt carried in its imagination vivid pictures of its old home (10). Cats, dogs, horses, and other animals dream, and parrots talk in their sleep. Horses and cattle sometimes stampede at imaginary objects, and often distort real objects into imaginary monsters. When a horse at night takes fright at a big black stump by the roadside, he no doubt imagines it to be some terrible creature ready to eat him up if he should go near it, just as a timid child does in the same circumstances. There is a great difference in horses in this respect, just as there is among children and men, some of them taking fright at every unusual thing, while others are more bold or stolid. The cat playing with a ball of yarn converts it by means of its imagination into an object of prey, just as a girl converts a doll into a baby, or a boy changes a stick into a steed. Sympathy is the putting or picturing of one's self in the place of another, and by means of the imagination sharing or simulating the psychic conditions of that other. This high and holy exercise of the imagination is exhibited by horses, cattle, dogs, deer, elephants, monkeys, and birds—in fact, by nearly all animals as far down as the fishes and insects.

Emotion is the stirring of the sensibilities by way of the intellect or the imagination. The following emotions are found in non-human beings : fear, surprise, affection, pugnacity, play, pride, anger, jealousy, curiosity, sympathy, emulation, resentment, appreciation of the beautiful, grief, hate, cruelty, joy, benevolence, revenge, shame, remorse, and appreciation of the ludicrous. Excepting the emotions of conscience and religion, which are really compounds, with fear as the main ingredient, this list of non-human emotions is co-extensive with the list of human emotions. Many of these emotions germinate low down in the animal kingdom, fear, anger, sexuality, and jealousy all being found in fishes and in the higher invertebrates. In the higher vertebrates many of these emotions are almost as strong as they are in men. Does anyone who has felt the throbbing sides of a frightened puppy or hare have any doubt that these creatures suffer the keenest agony of fear ? Apes have been known to fall down and faint when suddenly confronted by a snake, so great is their instinctive horror of serpents ; and gray parrots, which are extremely nervous birds, have been known to drop from their perch unconscious under the influence of great fear (14).

The horse is, perhaps, of all animals, the one which occasionally gives itself over most completely to the emotion of fear, as everyone who has witnessed the terrible abandon of a runaway team can testify. Ants, fishes, birds, cats, dogs, horses, monkeys, porpoises, and many other animals play. Young kittens, colts, and puppies enjoy a scuffle about as well as boys do. Pugnacity originates among the spiders and insects, and is highly developed in the ant, cock, and bulldog. This emotion is strong in the males of nearly all vertebrates. Anyone who has observed the vigilance displayed by fishes in protecting their nests can have little doubt that these comparatively primitive beings possess pugnacity. I was one evening floating in a boat by the edge of a Long Island pond just over a village of perches. Each nest was guarded by an assiduous male, who hovered over it vigilantly, or darted this way and that to drive off the piscatorial *hoi polloi* hanging about the neighbourhood, ready to slip in at the first opportunity and eat the eggs. Just to see what would happen, I put my hand down into the water and moved it slowly toward one of the nests. To my surprise, the guardian of the nest, instead of fleeing in alarm, proceeded to show fight. It chased my hand away time after time, and when the hand was not removed it would nip it vigorously, not once simply, but two or three times if necessary, and each time with increasing energy. It contended with the courage of a little hero. I pushed it and jostled it about, and even took it in my hand and lifted it clear out of the water. To my amazement, on getting back into the water, it returned promptly to the attack. It fought until it was really fagged, for its onsets were at last much feebler than at first. I came away after twenty minutes, leaving the little hero in triumphant possession of his charge.

Among some species of monkeys several individuals will join together in overturning a stone for the possible ants' eggs under it; and, when a burying beetle has found a dead mouse or bird, it goes and gets its companions to help it in the interment (20). Crows show benevolence by feeding their blind and helpless companions, and monkeys adopt the orphans of deceased members of their tribe. Brehm saw two crows feeding in a hollow tree a third crow which was wounded. They had evidently been doing this for some time, for the wound was several weeks old. Darwin tells of a blind pelican which was fed upon fishes, which were brought to it by its friends from a distance of thirty miles (15). The devotion of cedar-birds to each other and their kindness to all birds in distress are well known to every student of ornithology. Olive Thorne Miller tells of a cedar-bird that raised a brood of young robins that had been left orphans by the accidental killing of the parents. Weddell saw more than once during his journey to Bolivia that when a

herd of vicunas were closely pursued the strong
males covered the retreat of the weaker and less
swift members of the herd by lagging behind and
protecting them (20).

A remarkable instance of altruism which he
once saw exhibited by the king-crabs in a London
aquarium is mentioned by Kropotkin in his work
on 'Mutual Aid a Factor in Evolution.' One of
these crabs had fallen on its back in a corner of
the tank. And for one of these great creatures,
with its saucepan carapace, to get on its back
is, even in favourable circumstances, a serious
matter. The seriousness was increased in this
instance by an iron bar, which hindered the
normal activities of the unfortunate crustacean.
'Its comrades came to the rescue, and for one
hour's time I watched how they endeavoured to
help their fellow-prisoner. They came two at
once, pushed their friend from beneath, and after
strenuous efforts succeeded in lifting it upright.
But then the iron bar prevented them from achiev-
ing the work of rescue, and the crab again fell
heavily on its back. After many attempts, one of
the helpers went into the depth of the tank and
brought two other crabs, who began with fresh
forces the same pushing and lifting of their helpless comrade. We stayed in the aquarium for
more than two hours, and, when leaving, came to
cast a glance upon the tank. The work of
attempted rescue still continued. Since I saw
that I cannot refuse credit to the observation
quoted by Dr. Erasmus Darwin that the common

crab during the moulting season stations a sentinel, an unmolted or hard-shelled individual, to prevent marine enemies from injuring moulted individuals in their unprotected state.' Walruses go to the defence of a wounded comrade when summoned by its cries for help. Romanes tells of a gander who acted as a guardian to his blind consort, taking her neck gently in his mouth and leading her to the water when she wanted to take a swim, and after allowing her to cruise for a time under his guidance and care, conducting her back home again in the same thoughtful manner. When goslings were hatched, this remarkable gander seemed to realise the inability of the mother to look after them, for he took charge of them as if they were his own, convoying them to the waterside, and lifting them carefully out of the ruts and pits with his bill whenever they got into difficulty (10).

The disposition to go to the aid of a fellow in trouble is one of the most characteristic traits in the psychology of the swine. A single squeal of distress from even the scrawniest member of a swine herd will bring down on the one who causes this distress the hair-raising wrath of every porker within hearing. This trait has been considerably reduced by domestication, and in those varieties in which degeneracy has gone farthest it scarcely exists. But it is exceedingly strong in all wild hogs. Animals as low in the scale of development and as proverbially cold as snakes have been known, when educated and treated with kindness, to manifest considerable affection for their friends and masters. Nearly all domestic animals display a good deal of affection, not only to their young, but to adult members of their own kind and to their human masters. The devotion of the dog to man is without a parallel anywhere. It has been said that 'the dog is the only thing on this earth that loves you more than he loves himself.' When dogs become so much attached to their masters or mistresses that they pine and die on being separated from them, they show beyond any question that they have feelings which, in intensity, are not inferior to those possessed by the more highly developed men and women. And this has happened time after time.

A pathetic story of love and of its tragic close came last year out of the Maine woods. Two moose, who had been tracked all day by a couple of human tigers, were finally overtaken, when one of them fell pierced by two rifle-balls. The remaining moose, instead of dashing off into the forest, stood still, lowered its head, and sniffed at its fallen companion. Then, raising its antlers high into the air, it bellowed loudly. As the cry of the great creature echoed through the forest, it also fell at the discharge ot the rifles. It was found on examination afterwards that the first moose was blind, and that the second one, which had neglected to leave it for safety, was its pilot.

My father once owned a cow who contracted a strong affection for my sister. This cow, who showed on many occasions and in many ways her highly developed emotional nature, would scarcely allow anyone else than my sister to milk her. She always presented herself to my sister as soon as she was let into the lot in order to be milked first, and she was so jealous of this privilege that if it were not accorded to her she would stand with her head down and give vent to her unhappiness in low moans. After she was milked she would follow her human friend around from one cow to another, in order to be as near her as possible. She knew my sister's voice from that of everyone else, and would always low a response and come to her when called by name, even though she were a quarter of a mile away in the pasture. Romanes tells somewhere of a band of apes that were being pursued by dogs when a young ape was cut off from the rest and was about to be killed by the dogs. The chief of the band, seeing the peril of the young one, went deliberately back and rescued it.

Many animals show that they possess a rudimentary sense of humour by the pranks and tricks which they play on each other and on human beings. The monkey is the prince of non-human jokers, but dogs, cats, horses, elephants, and other animals have enough of this sense to have books written about it. A monkey has been observed to slyly pass his hand back of a second monkey and tweak the tail of a third one, and then composedly enjoy himself while the resentment of the injured monkey expended itself on the innocent middle one. Many monkeys enjoy entertaining their friends with grimaces, by carrying a cane, putting a tin dish on their heads, or other droll antics. These intelligent animals have a sufficiently high appreciation of the ludicrous to dislike ridicule. Like human beings, they can't endure being laughed at, and get mad if they are made the victims of a joke. Romanes' monkey was one day asked to crack a nut for the amusement of a visitor. The nut turned out to be a bad one, and the melancholy look of disappointment on the monkey's face caused the visitor to laugh. The insulted monkey flew into a rage, and hurled the nut at the offending scoffer, then the hammer, and finally the coffee-pot which simmered on the grate fire (10). Darwin tells of a baboon in the Zoological Gardens of London who always became infuriated every time his keeper took out a letter or book and read aloud to him. On one occasion when Darwin was present the baboon became so furious that he bit his own leg until it bled (15).

The emotion variously known as shame, regret, repentance, and remorse, is not common among the non-human races. It is found sometimes in dogs and monkeys, and especially in educated anthropoids. But this emotion is exceedingly rare among savages, and is not at all universal even among civilised societies of men. Some animals manifest self-restraint, which is an exceedingly elite quality of mind, and one not so common as it might be even among the higher breeds of mankind. By restraint is meant the inhibition of a desire or instinct in the presence of circumstances tending to render the desire or instinct active—and this is obedience, and the beginning of morality. A dog that will not chase a hare in the presence of his master may do so in his absence. I taught my guinea-pigs to abstain from certain food in their presence which they wanted very much, and which they would have eaten if they had not been educated to let it alone. Sympathy is the most beautiful of all terrestrial emotions. It is manifested, sometimes to an exceedingly touching degree, by all the highest races of animals. No other instances than those already given can be mentioned here. It is sufficient to say that the difference between the savage —whose sympathies are so feeble that he has been known to knock his own child's brains out for dropping a basket, and who puts his aged parents to death in order to avoid the burden of maintaining them, and whose sympathies seldom extend beyond his family or tribe—and civilised men and women, who feel actual pain when in the presence of those who suffer, and whose sympathies sometimes include all sentient creation, is much greater than that between the savage and many non-human animals. The frail, narrow, fantastic character of human sympathy is the most mournful fact in human nature. ' Man's inhumanity to man makes countless thousands mourn,' and his inhumanity to not-men makes the planet a ball of pain and terror.

Volition is the power of the mind to act executively. Or, perhaps, it is the resultant of the impulses actuating a mind at any particular instant. Whatever volition is, it is the same thing in the insect as in the man. Non-human beings have been observed to pause and deliberate and to make wise and momentous decisions in the twinkling of an eye. A chased hare will decide to squat, to go straight ahead, or to do something else which the emergency demands, just as unmistakably as a human fugitive. In the sense of being the power to act differently from the manner in which a being actually does act, there is no such thing as freewill. The will of the worm is just as free as the will of the judge—not in the sense that it is as varied in the directions of its activity, but in the sense that the character of its activities is determined inevitably by the character of its antecedents. All will, whether human or non-human, invariably acts in the direction of the strongest motive, just as a stone or a river invariably moves, if it moves at all, in the direction of the strongest tendency or force. It is impossible that this should be otherwise. For, if the will in any case elects to overthrow this fact by arbitrarily discarding a stronger motive for a feebler, in the very motive of the election are concealed elements which transform the feebler motive into the stronger. All motion, voluntary and involuntary—the motion of bullets, beings, societies, and suns—takes place along the lines of least arrest. Every being is compelled to decide as he does decide and to act as he does act by the inherited tendencies of his own nature and the tendencies of the environment in which he exists. And if any being, after having passed through life, were again placed back at the beginning of life and endowed with the same nature as before, and were acted upon through life by surroundings identical with those he had previously met, he would act—that is, he would exercise his will—in precisely the same way in every particular as he had previously done. To deny these things is to assert that the conduct of living beings is without law, and that psychology and sociology are not sciences.

Non-human beings, all of the higher ones, have the same brain and nervous apparatus as man, and in their involuntary phenomena they closely resemble human beings. Aim a pretended blow near the eyes of a dog or a horse and it will wink involuntarily, just as a human being does. Sever the spinal cord of a man or a frog, and irritate the feet of each, and they will each manifest the same phenomena of reflex action, drawing their feet away each time from the stimulus.

Instinct and *reason* are forms of intelligence. Intelligence is the adaptation of acts to ends. Intelligence is manifested by all organisms, both plants and animals, and may be either conscious or unconscious. Plant intelligence and reflex action are forms of *unconscious* intelligence. Plant intelligence, or the adaptation of acts to ends by plants, is manifested by plants in the shifting of their positions when in need of light in order to obtain as large a supply as possible of the essential sunshine; in devices, such as traps and flowers, for utilising the juices and services of insects; in germinating and growing away from, instead of toward, the centre of the earth; in discriminating between this and that kind of food; and in a thousand other ways.   Plant intelligence is all explicable in terms of chemistry and physics, and is, so far as is known, unaccompanied by consciousness.   Reflex action is chemical affinity aided by the co-ordinating powers of nerve tissue.   The vital processes of all animals, from the lowest to the highest, and many other highly habitual and highly essential operations, are carried on by reflex action.   Reflex action in animals, like plant intelligence, is unconscious.

Instinct and reason are *conscious*.   Instinct is inherited intelligence—intelligence manifested independently of, and prior to, experience and instruction. 'Instinct,' says Romanes, 'is reflex action into which has been imported the element of consciousness' (1).   It is exhibited by the babe when it nurses the mother's breast; by the chick when it pecks its way out through the shell of the egg; by animals generally, including man, in their solicitude for their young; by the parent bird in incubation; and by all beings when they seek food in obedience to the impulse of hunger.   Our conception of the mental processes of non-humans is as yet very primitive, owing to our limited means of information and the erroneous influence on our judgments of traditional ways of thinking;

and much that is attributed by us to instinct is not instinct at all, but is acquired by the young through education imparted by the elders. Parent birds have often been seen teaching their young ones to fly, and no doubt a good deal of the migratory acumen manifested by birds is nothing but custom and tradition handed down to each younger generation by the old and experienced. A large part of the knowledge of mankind (or what passes for knowledge) consists of habits and hobbies, customs and traditions, impressed upon each new generation by the generation which produced it. Each generation of men seems to feel that whenever it creates a new generation it has got to pile on to this new generation all of the fool notions which have been acquired from the past, amplified by its own inventions. And when we come to know other animals better, there is practically no doubt that we shall find that a large part of what we now call instinct and look upon as congenital will, on closer and more rational examination, be found to be nothing but the pedagogical effects of early environment. Professor Poulton, of Oxford, who has made many experiments on just-born birds, says that young chicks *learn* to fear the hawk and to interpret the oral warnings of the mother. Cats teach their young to play with their prey in that cruel manner so characteristic of all the Felidæ, as I have myself observed more than once. A mother cat will carry a live mouse into the presence of her kittens and lie down and play

with it, tossing it playfully into the air, poking it
with her paw when it does not move, and arresting
it when it starts to run away, the kittens all the
time looking on, but never once attempting to
take the mouse.   After awhile the mother hands
the captive over to the kittens, who go through the
same performance one after another.   After they
have practised on it until the unfortunate creature
is almost dead, the old cat will probably walk over
to where the mouse is and eat it up.   The whole
thing is a *school*.   The mouse is obviously not
intended as food for the young, but to be used
simply to impart instruction to them.

' In popular writings and lectures some or all of
the following activities of ant-life are commonly
ascribed to instinct : The recognition of members
of the same nest ; powers of communication ;
keeping aphides for the sake of their sweet secretions ; collection of aphid eggs in October, hatching them out in the nest, and taking them in the
spring to the daisies on which they feed, for
pasture ; slave-making and slave-keeping, which,
in some cases, is so ancient a habit that the
enslavers are unable even to feed themselves ;
keeping insects as beasts of burden—*e.g.*, a kind
of plant-bug to carry leaves ; keeping beetles, etc.,
as domestic pets ; habits of personal cleanliness—
one ant giving another a brush-up, and being
brushed up in return ; habits of play and recreation ; habits of burying their dead ; the storage of
grain and nipping the budding rootlet to prevent
further germination ; the habit of Texan ants of

preparing a clearing around their nest, and, six months later, harvesting the ant-rice—a kind of grass of which they are particularly fond—even seeking and sowing the grain which shall yield the harvest; the collection by other ants of grass to manure the soil, on which there grows a species of fungus upon which they feed; the military organisation of the ecitons of Central America; and so forth. But to class all of these activities of the ant as illustrations of instinct is a survival of an old-fashioned method of treatment.

'Suppose that the intelligent ant were to make observations on human behaviour as displayed in one of our great cities or in an agricultural district. Seeing so great an amount of routine work going on around him, might he not be in danger of regarding all this as evidence of hereditary instinct? Might he not find it difficult to obtain satisfactory evidence of the fact that this routine work has to some extent to be learned? Might he not say (perhaps not wholly without truth), " I can see nothing whatever in the training of these beings to fit them for their life-work. The training of their children has no more apparent bearing upon the activities of their after-life than the feeding of our grubs has on the duties of ant-life. They seem to fall into the routine of life with little or no preparatory training as the periods for the manifestation of the various instincts arrive. If learning thereof there be, it has so far escaped our observation. And such intelligence as their activities evince (and many of them do show remarkable adaptations to uniform conditions of life) would seem to be rather ancestral than of the present time, as is shown by the fact that many of the adaptations are directed rather to past conditions of life than to those which now hold good. In the presence of new emergencies to which their instincts have not fitted them, these poor creatures are often completely at a loss. We cannot but conclude, therefore, that, although acting under somewhat different and less favourable conditions, instinct occupies fully as large a space in the psychology of man as it does in that of the ant, while human intelligence is far less unerring and hence markedly inferior to our own."

'Are these views much more absurd than the views of those who, on the evidence which we at present possess, attribute all the activities of ant-life to instinct?' (21)

Reason is the power of adapting means to ends which is acquired from experience or instruction. All animals that profit by experience, therefore, or that learn from instruction—that is, are *teachable* —exercise reason.

The line of demarkation between instinct and reason is a mezzotint, reason being often instinctive, and instinct being as frequently flavoured with judgment. 'Instinct is usually regarded as a special property of the lower animals, and contrasted with the conscious reason of man. But just as reason may be looked upon as a higher form of the understanding or intellect, and not as something essentially distinct from them, so a closer examination shows that instinct and the conscious understanding do not stand in absolute contrast, but rather in a complex relation, and cannot be sharply marked off from each other.' It is instinct that urges the bird to build its nest ; but when birds whose habit it is to build on the ground learn, on the introduction of cats into the neighbourhood, to change their nesting-places to the tree-tops, intelligence and thought are necessary. The first time Cavy (one of my guinea-pigs) smelled a cat, she was almost scared to death. She jumped back from it as if she had come in contact with a red-hot stove, and screamed and kept on screaming, and shot down under my coat as if she were about to be crucified. After a little while I tried to pull her out, but she refused, and kept hiding. The second time the kitten was presented to her the result was the same. But after two or three days of association, she paid little more attention to it than to the other guinea-pigs. She had never seen a cat before. *It was the odour of the carnivore* that terrified her, and the effect was purely instinctive. But instinct was soon modified by intelligent experience. (*Poor dear little Cavy ! I wonder where she is now !*)

Both instinct and reason (and one, too, just as much as the other) are absolutely dependent upon processes that are purely mechanical—that is, upon brain processes ; and brain processes depend upon brain structure, which is inherited. Hence, reason is, in a certain sense, as truly inherited as instinct is. A being must be born with the particular nervous apparatus by means of which reasoning is carried on, or with the power or disposition to develop this apparatus, or he will never reason. The genius of the partridge in cajoling the passer-by from her nest is called instinct, but it is not more inherited than was the genius of Shakspere. Experience simply calls into being that, whatever it is in each particular being, which is inherited. Sir Isaac Newton took to philosophy and Ole Bull to music not less inevitably than the duck takes to water or the hound to hunting. Reason is, hence, inherited by every man, who has it as truly as his erect posture and plantigrade feet. There is something in the past of all of us and of everything which has determined, and which may be used to account for, everything that to-day exists or happens, even to the style and behaviour of every leaf that flutters in the forest, and to the eccentricities of our opinions and handwritings.

Reason, in the sense in which it is here used, is found feebly in the oyster. Oysters taken from a depth never uncovered by the sea open their shells, lose their water, and quickly perish. But oysters taken from the same depths, if kept where they are occasionally left uncovered for short intervals, learn to keep their shells closed and to live a much longer period out of the water. On the coast of France 'oyster schools' exist, where oysters intended for inland cities are educated to keep their shells closed when out of the water in order to enable them to survive the desiccating exposures of the overland journey (10). This act of the bivalve is probably the result of something like a vague form of reason. It is an act adapted to the accomplishment of a definite end, and the adapting power is acquired from experience. It is, moreover, reason which in its final analysis does not differ from the reason displayed by the wisest being that thinks. Judgment, forethought, common-sense, inference, ingenuity, genius, reason, and abstract thought, are all exercises of the cognitive or perceptive power of mind, and consist, all of them, in nothing more nor less than the discerning of relations among stimuli. The dog who adopts a cut-off in order to intercept a fleeing hare performs exactly the same kind of intellectual process as the mechanic who erects a windmill in order to divert the energies of the breeze, or the politician who adopts a particular platform to catch votes. ' A perception is always in its essential nature what logicians term a *conclusion*, whether it has reference to the simplest memory of the past sensation or to the highest product of abstract thought. For, when the highest product of abstract thought is analysed, the ultimate elements must always be found to consist in material given directly by the senses; and every stage in the symbolic construction of ideas, in which the process of abstraction consists, depends on acts of perception taking place in the lower stages' (1). The difference among the perceptive acts of different individuals consists, not in the different kinds of intellectual exercise, but in differences among the *materials* with which the perceptive faculty deals. There are perceptions of simple sensations, and there are perceptions of composite sensations, or concepts—perceptions of elementary relations, and perceptions of compound and elaborate relations. But all displays of rational faculty, from the simple judgment of distance by the dimness and distinctness of defini- tion and the size of the visual angle, which all higher animals are compelled to make, to the labyrinthic abstractions of the logician, consist in nothing in addition to discriminations among stimuli.

Brehm one day gave one of his apes a paper bag with a lump of sugar and a wasp in it. The ape in getting the sugar was stung by the wasp. From that day, whenever Brehm gave that ape, or any other ape in that cage, a paper package, the animal, before opening it, took the precaution to shake the package at his ear and listen to find out whether or not there was a wasp inside (18). Now, such an act of intelligence implies several inferences. A train of thoughts something like this must have passed through this ape's mind: ' Now, if one wasp can sting, so can another; and, if a man can deceive me once by wrapping a wasp in a paper with a lump of sugar, he may try it again ; and, if one man will attempt such a thing, so may another ; and, if men will attempt it on me, they may attempt it on my friends ; so I will warn my friends to look out for those villainous chaps outside.' These inferences of the ape are the same kind of generalisations exactly as are made by men everywhere in their daily lives. And the common-sense inferences made by ordinary people in their every-day affairs are precisely the same processes of reasoning as those used by scientists and philosophers. Many people, like the character in Molière's plays who was surprised and delighted to learn that he had been talking prose all his life, are surprised on hearing for the first time that they use *induction* and *deduction* every hour almost of their waking lives. They imagine that philosophers must have some secret and superior way of acquiring their conclusions, different from what ordinary mortals have. 'But there is no more difference,' says Huxley, 'between the mental operations of a man of science and those of an ordinary person than there is between the operations and methods of a grocer weighing out his goods in common scales and the operations of a chemist in performing a difficult and complex analysis by means of his balance and finely graduated weights. It is not that the scales in the one case and the balances in the other differ in the principles of their construction or manner of working; but the beam of the one is set on an infinitely finer axis than the other, and, of course, turns by the addition of a much smaller weight' (16). And the difference in mental method between the man of learning and the ordinary man or woman is the same as the difference between mature men and children and between men

generally and other animals. It is one of *degree,*
not of *kind.* The philosopher, the clodhopper,
and the ape, all use precisely the same methods
of reasoning, differing only in exactness and in
the materials of consciousness dealt with.

Nearly all animals, from mollusks to men,
reason—not once or twice in a lifetime, but the
most of them every day and every hour of their
existence. In fact, it would be impossible for any
animal addicted to moving about, and with a
delicate and easily wrecked organism, to long
survive in a world like this without that elasticity
of action which reason alone can impart. Since
they live in the same world-conditions as human
beings, and are seeking providence for substantially
the same wants, non-human beings manifest
reason in the same general directions as human
beings do—in the location and construction of
their homes and fortresses, in the arrest of their
prey, in circumventing their enemies, in over-
coming obstacles and surmounting dangers, in
protecting and educating their young, in meeting the emergencies of food and climate, in
the wooing of mates and the waging of wars,
and in the thousand other cases where they
are called upon in their daily wanderings and
doings to deal with novel and unprecedented
situations.

When wild geese are feeding there is said to be
always one of them that acts as sentinel. This
one never takes a grain of corn while on duty.
When it has acted awhile it gives the bird next to

it a sharp peck and utters a querulous kind of
cry, and the second one takes its turn. This is
prudence, or forethought, which is a form of
reason. When swans are diving there is generally
one that stays above the water and watches.
Sentinels have alarm sounds of various kinds,
which they give to signify ' enemy.' ' Ibex,
marmots, and mountain-sheep whistle; prarie-
dogs bark; elephants trumpet; wild geese and
swans have a kind of bugle call; rabbits and
sheep stamp on the ground; crows caw; and
wild ducks utter a low, warning quack.'

In the *Popular Science Monthly* for March, 1901,
is an account of a series of experiments on the
intelligence of the turtle made by Professor Yerkes,
of Harvard. The turtle was placed in a labyrinth,
at the farther end of which was a comfortable bed
of sand. It took just thirty-five minutes of wandering for the turtle to reach the nest the first time.
But in the second trial the nest was reached in
fifteen minutes, and by the tenth trip the turtle
was familiar enough with the route to go through
in three and one-half minutes, making but two
mistakes. The turtle was afterwards placed in a
more complex labyrinth, containing, among other
features, a blind alley and two inclines. The
inclines were puzzles, and it took one hour and
thirty-five minutes of aimless rambling for the
wanderer to reach its nest the first time. But
the fifth trip was made in sixteen minutes, and
the tenth in four minutes, which was not far from
direct.

These experiments show that animals of almost proverbial density may learn with surprising quickness. English sparrows and other avian inhabitants of the city learn to live tranquilly along the busiest thoroughfares, exposed to all sorts of dangers, and subjected to what would be to many birds the most terrifying circumstances. Whizzing trolleys, tramping multitudes, and screaming engines have no terrors for them. They simply exercise the caution necessary to keep from being run over. They boldly build their nests right under passing elevated cars, where the roar is sufficient to scare the life out of an ordinary country bird. I have seen these testy little chaps sit and feed and jabber to each other in a perfectly unconcerned way within ten or fifteen feet of a thundering express train. They do not do these things from instinct : they *learn* to do them. They know that a diabolical-looking locomotive is harmless, because they have seen it before; and they know that an insignificant urchin with a savage heart and a sling is not harmless, and they know it simply because they have previously had dealings with him. English sparrows will disappear completely from a neighborhood if a few of them are killed. Cats, dogs, horses—all animals, in fact—acquire during life a fund of information as to how to act in order to avoid harm and extinction. If they did not, they would not live long. And they do it just as man does it, by memory and discrimination, by retaining impressions made upon them, and acting differently when an impression is made a second, third, or thirteenth time.

Animals of experience (including men) are more skilful in adjusting themselves to environmental exigencies than the young and inexperienced, because of their store of initial impressions. It is a matter of common observation that young animals are more easily caught or killed or otherwise victimised than the old and experienced. Many animals, however, (and a good many men) are able to profit by a single impression. One dose of tartar emetic is generally sufficient to cure an egg-sucking dog, and it is a very stupid canine indeed that does not understand perfectly after one or two experiences with a porcupine or an unsavory skunk. 'The burnt child dreads the fire,' but so does the burnt puppy. Rengger states that his Paraguay monkeys, after cutting themselves only *once* with any sharp tool, would not touch it again, or would handle it with the greatest caution (10). Older trout are more wary than young ones, and fishes that have been much hunted and deceived become suspicious of traps. Rats, martins, and other animals cannot long be trapped in the same way, and partridges and other birds seldom fly against telegraph-wires the second season after the wires are put up. These animals, however, cannot learn to avoid these dangers from experience, for only a few of them are ever caught or struck. They must learn it from observing their unfortunate companions. Everyone who has read the story of Lobo, the big gray wolf of the

Carrumpaw, cannot but wonder at the remarkable shrewdness shown by this old leader in baffling for years the tigers that hung upon his tracks (17). Nansen states that the seals, before man invaded the Arctics, occupied the inner ice-floes to avoid the polar bear, but after man came they took to living on the outer floes in order to escape the persecutions of this new and more fearful enemy. Domestic animals, when first turned out in new regions, often die from eating poisonous weeds, but in some way soon learn to avoid them. Many animals, when pursuing other animals, or when being pursued, display a knowledge of facts very little understood by the majority of mankind, such as of places where scent lies or is obliterated, and the effects of wind in carrying evidence of their presence to their enemies. The hunted roebuck or hare will make circles, double on its own tracks, take to water, and fling itself for considerable distances through the air as cleverly as if it had read up all the theory of scent in a book. According to the London *Spectator*, one of the large African elephants in the Zoological Gardens of that city restores to its entertainers all the bits of food which on being thrown to him fall alike out of his reach and theirs. He points his proboscis straight at the food, and blows it along the floor to the feet of those who have thrown it. He clearly knows what he is about, for if he does not blow hard enough to land the food the first time, he blows harder and harder until he does. The cacadoos (parrots) of Australia, before descending upon a field or orchard in search of food, send out a scouting party to reconnoitre the region and see that 'all is well.' Sometimes a second party is sent. If the report is favourable, the whole band advance and plunder the field in short order. These birds are exceedingly wary and intelligent, and seldom make mistakes. But 'if man once succeeds in killing one of them, they become so prudent and watchful that they henceforward baffle all stratagems' (20). A short time ago a parrot at Washington, New Jersey, saved the life of its owner by summoning the neighbours to his relief. Cries of 'Murder!' 'Help!' 'Come quick!' coming from the home of the parrot, attracted the attention of neighbours, who ran to the house to find out the cause. 'They found the owner of the parrot lying on the floor unconscious, bleeding from a great gash in his neck. He had been repairing the ceiling, and had fallen and struck his head against the stove. It required six stitches to close the wound, and the surgeon said that in only a few minutes the injured man would have been dead. A few years ago this parrot's screams awakened its owner in time to arouse his neighbours and save them from a fire which started in the house next door.'

A friend of mine, who is thoroughly reliable, tells me that when he was a student at the University of Michigan a few years ago one of the professors of zoology there had a dog who was used by the department for experiments in digestion. The dog was compelled to wear a tube opening downward out of his stomach, and soon grew very weak and emaciated from the constant loss of food, which leaked out through this tube. After a time, however, the dog was observed to be growing unaccountably hale and strong. He was watched, and the poor creature was found to have struck upon an ingenious expedient to save his life. On eating his meal, he would go out to the barn, and, in order to prevent the artificial escape of the contents of his stomach, would lie down flat on his back between two boxes and remain there until his digested food had passed safely beyond the pylorus.

A few months ago, John, one of the monkeys at Lincoln Park, Chicago, was suffering from a terrible abscess on the cheek, and an operation became necessary in order to save the little fellow's life. It was a pathetic sight to see the look of trust in the monkey's eyes when the surgeon was ready to begin the operation, and the courage and fortitude displayed by the sufferer were almost human. At the first touch of the knife the monkey pressed his head hard against the knee of the assistant and grabbed the forefinger of each of the assistant's hands, just as a person does who is about to undergo a painful operation. The swelling was first cut open and washed with antiseptic, when the cheek-bone was scraped and a small piece of it removed. After being again washed in antiseptic, the wound was sewed up, and John was lifted gently back into his cage—not, however, until he had licked the hands of the surgeon and kissed his face in gratitude. The little hero never uttered a sound from the time the knife first touched his face until he was put back into his cage. A similar act of intelligence is recorded of an orang. Having been once bled on account of illness, and not feeling well some time afterward, this orang went from one person to another, and, pointing to the vein in his arm, signified his desire to have the operation repeated. Both of these instances are examples of reason of a very high order — of a higher order, indeed, than many children and some grown people exhibit in similar circumstances. The chimpanzee, Mafuca, learned how to unlock her cage, and stole the key and hid it under her arm for future use. After watching the carpenter boring holes with his brad-awl, she took the brad-awl and bored holes in her table. She poured out milk for herself at meals, and always carefully stopped pouring before the cup ran over.

When baboons go on marauding expeditions, they show that they realise perfectly what they are doing by moving with great stealth. Not a sound is uttered. If any thoughtless youngster so far forgets the necessities of the occasion as to utter a single chatter, he is given a reminder in the shape of a box on the ear. 'A certain Mr. Cops, who had a young orang, gave it half an orange one day, and put the other half away out of its sight on a high press, and lay down himself on the sofa. But the ape's movements, attracting his attention, he only pretended to go to sleep. The creature came cautiously and satisfied himself that his master was asleep, then climbed up the press, ate the rest of the orange, carefully hid the peel among the shavings in the grate, examined the pretended sleeper again, and then went and lay down on his own bed.' This incident is recorded by Tylor in his 'Anthropology.' 'And such behaviour,' he adds, 'is to be explained only by supposing a train of thought to pass through the brain of the ape somewhat similar to what we ourselves call reason.' These instances of undoubted intelligence and thought might be added to almost without number if there was room. Every person nearly who has been in the world any length of time, and has had occasion to associate with these so-called 'machines,' has seen for himself, often unexpectedly, many flashes of brightness among them.

It has been said that man differs from other animals, and is superior to them in the fact that he modifies his environment while other animals do not, but are modified by environment. Mr. Lester F. Ward makes this distinction in his 'Pure Sociology.' The distinction is no nearer the truth than other distinctions of like character that have from time to time been drawn between men and other animals. It is not much more than half true, if it is that, and does not by any means deserve the italics awarded to it by this writer. Many races of non-human beings have a far greater influence on their environment than many races of men have. Many tribes of men wander about naked, build no habitations, make no weapons, and feed upon the fruits, roots, insects, and such other chance morsels as they can pick up from day to day in their wanderings. Such races are far inferior in constructive activity to the birds, who build elaborate houses, and to the beavers, who not only construct substantial dwellings, but dam rivers, and cut down trees and transport them long distances, and dig artificial waterways, to be used as aids in their engineering enterprises. Compare the elaborate compartments of the Australian bower-birds, surrounded with ornamented and carefully-kept grounds, with the lean-to of many savage tribes, made by sticking two or three palm-leaves in the ground and leaning them against a pole. Even ants plant crops, make clearings, build roads and tunnels, etc. It must be remembered, too, that, however affirmative and masterful a race of men may become, it never succeeds, and never can succeed, in emancipating itself from the influences of environment. It is true that with the growth of intelligence among organic forms there has been a constant transfer of influence from the environment to the organism; but this transfer began, not with man by any means, but low down in the scale of animal life.

It has been said that man is the only animal that uses tools. But this is not true either, for animals as low in the scale of development as insects have been known to use tools. At least two different observers testify to having seen ground-wasps use small stones as hammers in packing the dirt firmly over their nests. Spiders

use stones as weights to steady their webs in times
of storm. Orangs throw sticks and stones at their
pursuers, and certain tribes of Abyssinian baboons,
when they go to battle with each other, carry
stones as missiles. Monkeys often use stones to
crack nuts with, and tame monkeys know very
well how to use a hammer when it is given to
them. In the London Zoological Gardens a
monkey with poor teeth kept a stone hidden in the
straw of its cage to crack its nuts with, and it
would not allow any other monkey to touch the
stone. 'Here,' says Darwin, in speaking of this
case, ' is the idea of property.' Monkeys also use
sticks as levers in prying open chests and lifting
heavy objects. Cuvier's orang used to carry a
chair across the room and stand on it to lift the
door-latch. Chimpanzees, who are very fond of
making a noise, have been seen standing around a
hollow log in the forest, beating it with sticks ;
and if we are to believe Emin Pasha, these ingenious parodies of men sometimes carry torches
when they go at night on foraging expeditions.
The Indian elephant, when travelling, will sometimes turn aside and break off a leafy branch from
a roadside tree and carry it along in its trunk to
sweep off the flies. As Dr. Wesley Mills says in
his work on ' The Nature and Development of
Animal Intelligence,' ' It was formerly believed
that animals cannot reason, but only those persons
who do not themselves reason about the subject,
with the facts before them, can any longer occupy
such a position.'

V. Conclusion.

It is enough. The ancient gulf scooped by human conceit between man and the other animals has been effectually and forever filled up. The human species constitutes but one branch in the gigantic arbour of life. And all the merit and all the feeling and all the righteousness of the world are not, as we have been accustomed to aver, congested into this one branch. And all of the weakness and deformity are not, as we have also been anxious to believe, found elsewhere. The reluctance of wrinkles and deformities to appear in the pictures of men, and of strength and beauty to appear in the representations of the other races of the earth, is to be accounted for by the highly elucidative fact that man is the universal portrait-painter. There is no one to tell man what he is and how he strikes others, and hence he is the 'paragon of creation'—the inter-stellar pet, half clay and half halo—the image and pride of the gods—the flower and gem of the eternal spheres. Man is the only professional linguist in the universe. And it is fortunate for him that he is. For, if he were not, his auditories would be compelled to carry to his perceptive centres a great many sentiments he now never hears. He would be likely to hear a good deal said, and said with a good deal of feeling, about perpendicular brigand—grandiloquent kakistocrat swelling with self-righteousness—rhetorical hideful wrapped in pillage and gorged with decomposition—a voluble and sanctimonious squash with two sticks in it. The definition of man as it appears in the dictionary of the donkey probably runs something like this: 'Man is an animal that walks on its hind-legs, invents adjectives with which to praise itself, and displays its greatest utility in proving that all sharks are not aquatic.' We know what a lion looks like when painted by a man, but human eyes have never yet been allumined by the sardonic lineaments of a man painted by a lion. Being boiled alive in order to look well as corpses in store-windows, and having wooden pegs thrust into our muscles and left there to rot for a week or two to keep us in our agony from doing something desperate—we know what these experiences are like when they are delegated to lobsters, and we take no more serious part in them than to insure their infliction, but we are too fervent barbarians to bother our heads about what they are like from the crustacean point of view.

Let us be candid. Men are not all gentle men and humane, and not-men are not all inhuman. There are reptiles in broadcloth, and there are warm and generous hearts among those peoples who have so long suffered from human prejudice and ferocity. Let us label beings by what they are—by the souls that are in them and the deeds they do—not by their colour, which is pigment, nor by their composition, which is clay. There are philanthropists in feathers and patricians in fur, just as there are cannibals in the pulpit and saurians among the money-changers. The golden rule may sometimes be more religiously observed in the hearts and homes of outcast quadrupeds than in the palatial lairs of bipeds. The horse, who suffers and serves and starves in silence, who endures daily wrongs of scanty and irregular meals, excessive burdens and mangled flanks, who forgets cruelty and ingratitude, and does good to them that spitefully use him, and submits to crime without resistance, misunderstanding without murmur, and insult without resentment, is a better Christian, a better exemplar of the Sermon on the Mount, than many church-goers, in spite of the creeds and interdictions of men. And the animal who goes to church on Sundays, wearing the twitching skins and plundered plumage of others, and wails long prayers and mumbles meaningless rituals, and gives unearned guineas to the missionary, and on week-days cheats and impoverishes his neighbours, glorifies war, and tramples under foot the most sacred principles of morality in his treatment of his non-human kindred, is a cold, hard-hearted *brute*, in spite of the fact that he is cunning and vainglorious, and towers about on his hinders.

There are lessons that may be learned from the uncorrupted children of Nature—lessons in simplicity of life, straightforwardness, humility, art, economy, brotherly love, and cheerfulness— more beautiful, perhaps, and more true than may sometimes be learned from the stilted and Machiavellian ways of men. Would you learn forgiveness? Go to the dog. The dog can stand more abuse

and forgive greater accumulations of wrong than
any other animal, not even excepting a wife.
About the only thing in the universe superior to
the dog in willingness to undergo outrage is the
human stomach. Would you learn wisdom and
industry ? Go to the ant, that tireless toiler of
the dust. The ant can do that which no man
can do—keep grain in a warm, moist atmosphere
without sprouting. Would you learn art ? Go
to the bee or to the wild bird's lodge. The art
of the honeycomb and of the hang-bird's nest
surpasses that of the cranny of the savage as
the Cathedral of St. Peter exceeds the cottage.
Would you learn socialism, that dream of poets
and the hope and expectation of wise men ? It is
actualised around you in thousands of insect
communities. The social and economic relations
existing in the most highly wrought societies of
bees and wasps are fundamentally the ideal relations of living beings to each other, but it will
require millenniums of struggle and bloodshed
for men to come up to them. Would you learn
curiosity—not the curiosity that gossips and
backbites, but the curiosity of the explorer and
searcher after knowledge ? Go to the monkey.
The monkey has been known to work two hours,
without pause, utterly unconscious of everything
but its purposes, trying to open a fettered trunk
lock (10). Would you learn sobriety ? Go not
to the gilded hells of cities, where men die like
flies in gin's vile miasma. Go to the spring where
the antelope drinks. Would you learn chastity ?

Go not to the foul dens and fiery chambers of men. Go to the boudoir of the bower-bird, or to the subterranean hollow where the wild wolf rears her litter.

Man is not the surpassingly pre-eminent individual he so actively advertises himself to be. Indeed, in many particulars he is excelled, and excelled seriously, by those whom he calls 'lower.' The locomotion of the bird is far superior in ease and expedition to the shuffling locomotion of man. The horse has a sense which guides it through darkness in which human eyes are blind; and the manner in which a cat, who has been carried in a bag and put down miles away, will turn up at the back-door of the old home next morning dumfounds science. The eye of the vulture is a telescope. The hound will track his master along a frequented street an hour behind his footsteps, by the imponderable odour of his soles. The cat-bird, without atlas or geographic manuals, will find her way back over hundreds of trackless leagues, season after season, to the same old nesting-place in the thicket. Birds, thousands of them, journey from Mexico to Arctic America, from Algiers and Italy to Spitzbergen, from Egypt to Siberia, and from Australia and the Polynesian Islands to New Zealand, and build their nests and rear their young, year after year, in the same vale, grove, or tundra. The nightingale, who pours out his incomparable lovesong in the twilight of English lanes during May and June, winters in the heart of Africa; and some birds nest within the

Arctic Circle and winter in Argentina. Some of the plovers travel the entire length of the American land mass every summer, from Patagonia to the Arctic Circle, in order to lay three or four pale-green eggs, and see them turn to birdlings by the shores of the Hudson Sea. Many animals have the power to foretell storms, and man, though he can weigh worlds, is ever glad to profit by their superior sense. When herons fly high above the clouds, when sea-birds dip and sport in the water and the bittern booms from the marshes, when swallows fly low and the sow repairs her bed, when horses scamper and cattle sniff the air, when ravens beat the air with their wings, make noises, and flock together, when the swan raises her eggs by additions to her nest and the prairie-dog scratches the dirt up around its hole, when beetles are not found in the air and caterpillars mass in their webs, when bees remain near their hives and ants carry their eggs to their innermost abodes, when frogs croak more loudly from their watery retreats and fishes seek the safety of the unharried deeps—look out for foul weather! Man has not the sweetness of the song-sparrow, the innocence of the fawn, nor the high relative brain capacity of the tomtit and the fice.

Many animals have powers by which they are able to act in concert at times, vast numbers of them moving in unison over immense areas by signals or intuitions which man can neither imitate nor understand. Such are the mysterious migrations of the Norway lemming and of many birds and insects, and such were the memorable stampedes of the bison hordes on the American plains in years gone by. Kropotkin saw on the Siberian steppes one autumn ' thousands and thousands ' of fallow deer come together from an area as large as Great Britain at a point on the Amur River in an unprecedented exodus to the lowlands on the other side (20). How these scattered thousands knew when to start so as to arrive at the river at the same time, and how they knew the direction to travel and found their way so well, are mysteries which man can as yet only wonder at. More marvellous yet—more marvellous, perhaps, than the concurrent action of any other animal, for it implies the most accurate time-keeping extending over many years—are the annual festivals of the *palolo*, an annelid living among the interstices of the coral reefs of some of the islands of the South Pacific. About three o'clock on the morning following the third quarter of the October moon, these worms invariably appear on the surface of the sea, swarming in great numbers. Just after sunrise their bodies begin to break to pieces, and by nine o'clock no trace of them is left. On the morning following the third quarter of the November moon they appear again, but usually in smaller numbers. After that they are seen no more till the next October. This annual swarming is a phenomenon connected with reproduction, the ova escaping from the broken bodies of the females and, after being fertilised by the free-floating sperms, sinking down among the coral reefs and hatching into a new generation. ' Year after year these creatures appear according to lunar time. And yet in the long-run they keep solar time. They keep two cycles, one of three and one of twenty-nine years. In the three-year cycle there are two intervals of twelve lunations and one of thirteen lunations. These thirty-seven lunations bring lunar time somewhat near to solar time. But in twenty-nine years there is enough difference to require the addition of another lunation; the twenty-ninth year is therefore one of thirteen instead of twelve lunations. In this way they do not change their season in an entire century. So unfailing is their appearance that in Samoa they have given their name to the spring season, which is called "the time of the palolo." '

Instead of the highest, man is in some respects the lowest, of the animal kingdom. Man is the most unchaste, the most drunken, the most selfish and conceited, the most miserly, the most hypocritical, and the most bloodthirsty of terrestrial creatures. Almost no animals, except man, kill for the mere sake of killing. For one being to take the life of another for purposes of selfish utility is bad enough. But the indiscriminate massacre of defenceless innocents by armed and organised packs, *just for pastime*, is beyond characterisation. The human species is the only species of animals that plunges to such depths of atrocity. Even vipers and hyenas do not exterminate for recreation. No animal, except man, habitually seeks wealth purely out of an insane impulse to accumulate. And no animal, except man, gloats over accumulations that are of no possible use to him, that are an injury and an abomination, and in whose acquisition he may have committed irreparable crimes upon others. There are no millionaires—no professional, legalised, lifelong kleptomaniacs—among the birds and quadrupeds. No animal, except man, spends so large a part of his energies striving for superiority—not superiority in usefulness, but that superiority which consists in simply getting on the heads of one's fellows. And no animal practises common, ordinary morality to the other beings of the world in which he lives so little, compared with the amount he preaches it, as man.

Let us be honest. Honour to whom honour is due. It will not emaciate our own glory to recognise the excellence and reality of others, or to come face to face with our own frailties. We *are* our brother's keeper. Our brethern are they that feel. Let us universalise. Our thoughts and sympathies have been too long wingless. *The Universe is our Country, and our Kindred are the Populations that Mourn. It is well*—it is eminently well, for it is godlike—*to send our Magnanimity to the Dusts and the Deeps, our Sunrises to the Uttermost Isles, and our Charity to the Stars.*

BIBLIOGRAPHY

(1) ROMANES: Mental Evolution in Animals ; New York, 1898.

(2) BURTON : First Footsteps in East Africa ; London, 1856.

(3) LUBBOCK : Origin of Civilisation ; New York, 1898.

(4) DEMOOR : Evolution by Atrophy ; New York, 1899.

(5) DARWIN : Expression of Emotions in Men and Animals ; New York, 1899.

(6) STARR : Human Progress ; Meadville, Pennsylvania, 1895.

(7) HARTMANN : Anthropoid Apes ; New York, 1901.

(8) BREHM : From North Pole to Equator ; London, 1896.

(9) STANLEY: In Darkest Africa, vol i. ; New York, 1890.

(10) ROMANES : Animal Intelligence ; New York, 1899.

(11) EVANS : Evolutional Ethics and Animal Psychology ; New York, 1898.

(12) JESSE: Gleanings in Natural History, vol. i. ; London, 1832.

(13) PECKHAM AND PECKHAM : Instincts and Habits of the Solitary Wasps ; Madison, Wisconsin, 1898.

(14) CORNISH: Animals of To-day ; London, 1898.

(15) DARWIN : Descent of Man ; London, 1874.

(16) HUXLEY: On the Origin of Species, lecture iii.

(17) THOMPSON : Wild Animals I have Known ; New York, 1900.

(18) BREHM: Thierleben ; Leipzig, 1880.

(19) GILBRAITH : *Ethnological Journal*, 1869, p. 304.

(20) KROPOTKIN: Mutual Aid a Factor of Evolution ; New York, 1902.

(21) MORGAN : Animal Behaviour ; London, 1900.

THE ETHICAL KINSHIP

One of the wisest things ever said by one of the profoundest philosophers of all time was the warning to the seeker after truth to beware of the influence of the 'idols (or illusions) of the tribe,' by which he meant that body of traditional prejudices which every sect, family, nation, and neighbourhood has clinging to it, and in the midst of which and at the mercy of which every human being grows up.

THE ETHICAL KINSHIP

I. Human Nature a Product of the Jungle.

THE Golden Rule is not exemplified by the conduct of any considerable number of the inhabitants of the earth. To be civilised or even half-civilised is, to the children of this world, neither instinctive nor easy. To preserve a certain pretence or appearance of virtue, especially when encouraged to do so by an uplifted cudgel in the hands of the community, is a possible and not uncommon accomplishment. But to be at heart and in reality as considerate of others as we are of ourselves is, unfortunately, not natural. Human beings are not children of the sun, sojourning for a season on this spheroid of clay, and needing only pinions to be angels. Human nature did not come, pure and shining, down from the glittering gods. It came out of the jungle. Civilised peoples are the not very remote posterity of savages, and savages are the posterity of individuals who laid eggs and had literally cold blood in their veins. Civilised men and women are troglodytes with a veneering of virtue. In the heart of every ' civilised ' man and woman is an unconverted core, large or small, of barbarism. Humanity is only a habit. Against it, and tending ever to weaken and subvert it, are the powerful inertias of animalism. Like the ship in Ibsen's ' Rhymed Epistle,' civilisation carries a corpse in its cargo—the elemental appetites and passions which have been implanted in all sentient nature by the laws in accordance with which organic forms have been fashioned. Moral progress is simply the sloughing off of this inherited animality.

To the initiated, therefore, it is not strange that we civilised folk in our conduct display so freely the phenomena of the savage. There is nothing more inevitable in the life of the convert than the haunting inclination to give way to original impulses. It is not strange that we are powerless to be as good and beautiful and true as we would like to be, that our divine efforts are our half-hearted efforts, and that the only time we get terribly in earnest and put forth really titanic energies is when we are dominated directly or indirectly by the instincts of the pack. Human aspiration is fettered by the fearful facts of human origin. It is not strange that we are continually conscious of being torn by contending tendencies, conscious of ghastly masteries, and of horrible goings on in our innermost beings. The human heart is the gladiatorial meeting-place of gods and beasts.

II. Egoism and Altruism.

Everything has been evolved—*everything*—from daffodils to states and from ticks to religion. Every organic thing is the result of long and incessant survival of the advantageous—advantageous from the standpoint of the organism itself or from the standpoint of its kind, not necessarily so from the standpoint of the universe. That which is true of everything is true also of egoism and altruism. Egoism and altruism exist as facts in the natures of human and other beings for the same reason that the various physical facts exist in the structures of human and other beings, because they have been advantageous in the struggle for life. There is just as definite an explanation for the existence of egoism and altruism in this world, and for their existence in the particular form and ratio in which they do exist, as there is for the fact that the human hand has five fingers, the rose odour, and the eggs of the kildeer the mottled markings of the clods among which they lie.

Egoism is preference for self, partiality toward that part of the universe bounded by one's own skin. It may consist simply of regard for self, but with regard for self is usually associated enmity toward others. Egoism manifests itself in such qualities of mind as selfishness, cruelty, intolerance, hate, hardheartedness, savagery, rudeness, injustice, narrowness, and the like. It is the primal impulse of the living heart. Enmity is older and more universal than love. Enmity constituted the very loins from which long ago came the original miscreants of this world.

' I saw the fishes playing there ;
I saw all that was in the whole world round ;
In wood, and bower, and marsh, and mead, and field,
All things which creep and fly,
And put a foot to earth.
All these I saw, and say to you,
That nothing lives among them without hate.'

Life has been developed through selection. This selection has been brought about largely through war—war between individuals and between groups of individuals. War and competition are struggle between living beings, and the soul of competition is selfishness. Egoism is the primal and most powerful of terrestrial impulses, because beings hated and exterminated each other before they tolerated and loved, and because struggle has far overshadowed cooperation as a factor in life evolution.

There are those who believe that mutual aid has been a more dynamic factor in the development of terrestrial life than competition. Cooperation has been an important element in the evolution of animal life, and it has operated among nearly all animals, from the humblest to the highest. Far down near the beginning of organic existence we find the one-celled forms huddling together in colonies, giving rise in the course of time to the many-celled animals. But to conclude that cooperation is the chief factor in animal development is to shut one's eyes to one of the most obvious and overwhelming facts of organic evolution. Individualism antedates mutualism, both among the one-celled forms and among the many-celled metazoa. Cooperation everywhere is the sequence of a long preliminary of individual contention. And cooperation does not mean cessation of struggle, either among those co-operating or among the groups themselves, as Kropotkin and other exaggerators of the mutual aid factor seem to assume. It usually does little more than transfer the struggle from individuals to groups. When a lot of pelicans or wolves get together and work together in order that they may thereby the better defend themselves or slay others, it is hard to see how such facts can be placed to the credit of cooperation any more than to that of competition. Then, too, excepting in a few societies of insects, cooperation has not gone so far as to do more than slightly alleviate the competition even among the members of a co-operating group. Competition is a much more common and influential fact in the phenomena of life than cooperation, for it involves a large part of the activity of individual life, and is also promi-nent in all social activities.

The preponderance of egoism in the natures of living beings is the most mournful and immense fact in the phenomena of conscious life. It has made the world the kind of world it would have been had the gods actually emptied their wrath vials upon it. Brotherhood is anomalous, and, even in its highest manifestations, is but the expression of a veiled and calculating egoism. Inhumanity is everywhere. The whole planet is steeped in it. Every creature faces an inhospitable universeful, and every life is a campaign. It has all come about as a result of the mindless and inhuman manner in which life has been developed on the earth. It has been said that an individual of unlimited faculties and infinite goodness and power made this world and endowed it with ways of acting, and that this individual, as the world's executive, continues to determine its phenomena by inspiring the order of its events. But one cannot help thinking sometimes, when, in his more daring and vivid moments, he comes to comprehend the real character and condition of the world, what a discrepancy exists between the reputation of this builder and his works, and cannot help wondering whether an ordinary human being with only common-sense and insight and an average concern for the welfare of the world would not make a great improvement in terrestrial affairs if he only had the opportunity for a while.

Altruism is the recognition of, and regard for, others. It shows itself in feelings of justice, goodwill, tenderness, charity, pity, public spirit, sympathy, fraternity and love, and in acts of kindness, humanity, mercy, generosity, politeness, philanthropy and the like. Altruism is a graft. The stock is selfishness and brutality. Altruism (the form of altruism to which I here refer : there are several distinct species of altruism) has come into the world as a result of cooperation and consanguinity. It has grown out of the cooperation of individuals in families and tribes against their cooperating enemies. Altruism—at least, in its initial stages—is a sort of tribal egoism. Men and other animals have learned to stand by each other and help each other against their common foes because it was the only way in which they were able to stand. Those aggregates that have had strongest this feeling of fraternity have prospered and prevailed, while the less fraternal have gone down.

The altruism manifested by men in their relations with each other is not different in kind from the altruism and cooperation displayed by other social animals. Human gregariousness—the gathering together of human beings into tribes and communities for purposes of companionship and defence—is a part of the phenomena of animal gregariousness in general. The inhabitants of a human town, however much they may think so, are not impelled to associate with each other and to cooperate with each other in the affairs of life by causes or considerations different from those which actuate a society of ants or apes, of wasps or wolves, who do the same things. The antecedents of human ethics and society are, therefore, to be looked for in the ant-hill and the jungle.

The fact that altruism has been evolved by the cooperation of individuals *with each other* and *against others* is a significant fact in the analysis and understanding of the ethical phenomena of the earth. *To this fact is due the restricted and illogical character of all altruism.* The ethical systems of all peoples are, and have always been, to a greater or less extent, provincial and contradictory. Ethical feeling and practice are not extended universally—that is, to *all* beings—but are maintained only among those associating more or less closely as a group, and having interests that are more or less nearly the same. Among men of primitive mind, morality is a thing to be practised toward only a few thousand or even a few hundred individuals, and then in a very half-awake and half-hearted manner. But as the perceptions sharpen and vivify and the horizon of knowledge widens—as commerce and imagination cause the mind to overflow the narrow bounds of the community into larger dimensions of time and space—as the myriad influences operating as race experience and race selection enable men to realise the wider and wider oneness of their origin, natures, interests, and destiny— an increasing consistency characterises the conduct among the members of the group, and an increasingly larger number of individuals are admitted to ethical consideration and kinship.

III. The Ethics of the Savage.

The ethics of the savage is, almost without exception, purely tribal in its extent. A marked distinction is everywhere made by primitive peoples between injuries to persons *inside* the tribe and injuries to those *outside* the tribe. Crimes which are looked upon as felonious when committed by a savage against the members of his own tribe may be regarded as harmless, or even highly commendable, when perpetrated on those outside the tribe. Acts are not judged according to their intrinsic natures or results, but wholly as to whether they are performed on outsiders or on insiders. The Balantis (Africa) punish with death a theft committed against a fellow-tribesman, but encourage and reward thieving from other tribes. The Afridi (Afghanistan) mother prays that her son may be a successful robber—not a robber of her own people, but of other peoples—and in order that he may become proficient in crime teaches him to creep stealthily through a hole in the wall. By certain Bedouin tribes the 'strenuous life' is held in such high honour that 'it is considered a disgrace to die in bed'; and among the man-eating Fijians 'men who have not slain an enemy suffer the most degrading of all punishments' (1). In the paradise of the Kukis (India) the cut-throats who have in life killed the largest number of aliens not only inherit the highest places, but these adepts of the knife are supposed to be attended in their celestial comings and goings by their victims as slaves (1). In his dealings with the other members of his tribe, the savage observes a certain rude code of morals, this code being usually, as in the case of the civilised code, an inglorious mixture of equity and brutality, superstition and sanity, honesty and hypocrisy. But the savage recognises no moral obligations to any being outside of his tribe, clan, or family. Anthropology teaches nothing more positively than this. Consanguinity and self-interest are the only bases of savage friendship. Outsiders are outlaws. They may be attacked, robbed, deceived, murdered, eaten, or enslaved, with perfect propriety. It was this general hostility of foreigners that Cain feared when he was turned out from his countrymen after his crime upon Abel. He knew that he was liable to be set upon by the first stranger that came upon him. So the Lord is said to have set a mark upon him, 'lest any finding him should kill him.'

'There was no brotherhood recognised by our savage forefathers,' says Sir Henry Maine, in speaking of the ancestors of the Aryan and Semitic races, 'except actual consanguinity regarded as a fact. If a man was not of kin to another, there was nothing between them. He was an enemy to be hated, slain, or despoiled as much as the wild beasts upon which the tribe made war, as belonging, indeed, to the craftiest and cruelest of wild animals. It would scarcely be too strong to assert that the dogs which followed the camp had more in common with it than the tribesmen of an alien and unrelated tribe' (2). Among some tribes of savage men the ethical code is reversed in dealing with outsiders, and enmity toward aliens is considered a duty.

This same senseless hostility toward every one from abroad, so spitefully exhibited by primitive men, is also manifested by ants, who immediately recognise and pounce upon an individual introduced from a foreign colony, but welcome with every demonstration of joy, even after a lapse of weeks or months, a returning member of their own society. The same spirit of exclusiveness is found also in elephants. If by accident an elephant becomes separated from his herd, he becomes an outcast and a fugitive, never being permitted in any circumstances to attach himself to another herd (3).

That the savage should entertain feelings of friendship for those belonging to the same social unit as himself is, considering the circumstances in which it takes place, a perfectly natural phenomenon. The members of his tribe are, to the savage, the beings among whom he has come into existence, and in the midst of whom he has grown up. He knows and understands them, and is known and understood by them. They speak the same language as himself, and cherish the same customs and traditions. They have the same sacred trees, the same gods, the same experiences day after day, and the same memories, as he himself. They are his associates in the chase, his allies in war, and his comrades in sorrow and success. They are the only beings into whose lives he has ever entered. They constitute his world, and are to him the only real beings in the universe.

The members of his tribe are, moreover, to the savage, for the most part, his kinspeople. If they are not actually related to him by blood, they are usually conceived by him to be so related. The co-villagers of an Indian community call each other brothers. It is a characteristic of all the Aryan and Semitic races when in the tribal state to conceive that the tribes themselves, and all subdivisions of them, are descended each from a single male ancestor. The savage sees the living family of which he forms a part descended from a single living man and his wife or wives. This family group with which he is familiar and other similar groups make up the tribe. And the process by which each family has been brought about is in his mind identical with the process by which the community as a whole has been formed (2). It is a conception of this kind, handed down as a tradition from ancient tribal times, which causes the Jews even to-day to regard themselves as the 'seed' of that venerable sheik who, so many centuries ago, led them as a band of nomads in their memorable migration westward from the plains of Mesopotamia. It is not strange, therefore, considering all of the circumstances in the midst of which the savage lives and moves, that he should look upon his fellow-tribesmen as beings to be distinguished by him from all other beings in the universe.

Nor is it strange, when we consider the mental sterility of the savage, his lack of travel and imagination, the meagerness of his experiences, and his utter ignorance of the world beyond the community in which he lives, that he should look upon and treat all outsiders as nobodies—as beings without any claims whatever upon his humanity or mercy. The imagination is the picturing power of the mind, the power by which beings are able to get out of themselves and into the places of others, the power which enables us to view the world comparatively—that is, from different points of view. This power of mind, which imparts to the higher types of intelligence their mobility and sympathy, is rudimentary in the savage. This has been proved by Tylor in his study of the comparative mythology of savages. It is this lack of imagination in the savage, combined with his ignorance and his simplicity of life, which gives to him his ferocity, and which renders him inaccessible to those higher sentiments of justice and righteousness which are—well, which are, at least, dreamed about and theorised about by the more evolved savages of the 'civilised world.' The world, to the simple mind of the savage, is, as it is to the mind of the child, the world in which he lives and moves—the world which he feels, hears, tastes, and sees. The horizon is the boundary of the universe. Beings beyond his tribe are outside of the world. If they exist at all, it is as a very different order of beings from him and his people. They are not of kin to him, speak a strange tongue, and have monstrous customs and superstitions. How could they be in any way related to him? They are his enemies—vague, villainous apparitions who appear to him only in the horrible ordeals of battle. His chief occupation is the waging of war against them, and his keenest gratification is felt in laying them low. The accounts of all travellers testify that the intertribal relations of savages are, with few exceptions, those of chronic feud and hostility. The irreconcilable antagonism between the savage and those around him begets in the savage nature its dominating impulse—*hate*, hatred and hostility toward other men, as well as toward all other beings. In fact, the savage makes no moral distinction between man and the other animals, but regards them all indiscriminately as his foes, whom he must either use or remove from the face of the earth. The savage hunts men about as he hunts other animals, and for a like purpose. The Troglodytes hunted the Ethiopians in four-horse chariots with as little compunction as Americans hunt antelopes to-day.

IV. The Ethics of the Ancient.

But the doctrine that each petty tribe is the centre of the world and the only real and important people in the universe, and that all others are mere nobodies, is not peculiar to primitive peoples. Ethnocentric ethics—the ethics of amity toward their own tribe or state, their own clique or kind, and the ethics of enmity toward outsiders—has been manifested to a greater or less extent by the peoples of all times and of all degrees of enlightenment. Every people that has ever existed has had its own particular point of view, its own bias, its own knot-hole, large or small, through which it has looked at life and the world. This is inevitable. It arises as a necessary sequence out of the fact that all peoples above savages are the descendants of savages, and as such have inherited the limitations, mental and environmental, of those from whom they have evolved.

Aliens had no legal rights in ancient times— none whatever. International cooperation, such as exists among the political societies of Europe and America to-day, was absolutely unknown. International relations were everywhere those of hostility. States and races looked upon each other as foes, as objects of plunder and victimisation, not as friends.

Cæsar says of the ancient Germans that depredations committed beyond the boundaries of each state bore no infamy, and that stealing from aliens was even encouraged as a means of teaching their young men adroitness.

The ancient Jews are an excellent illustration of a narrow and self - centred people. Notwithstanding their insignificance, politically and intellectually, as compared with the Egyptians, Greeks, and Persians, the Jews believed themselves to be the only people of the first class inhabiting the earth. They conceived that they had been selected as favourites by the gods themselves, and that around their little district in half-arid Palestine revolved the interests of the entire world. Their chief city was supposed to be the sacred and central city of the world, and heaven itself only a new and idealised edition of their metropolis. Every Jew was bound to every other Jew by high-wrought ceremony and obligation. But all non-Jews were ' Gentiles,' chaff-like 'pagans,' who possessed no rights which a ' child of Abraham ' was bound to respect. Their tribal god is said to have been so indulgent toward them as his ' chosen people ' that he allowed them to exact usury from foreigners, to sell them diseased meats, and to borrow jewels from them and afterwards run away with them. He even permitted them to make war upon weak peoples and dispossess them of their lands. ' Whomsoever the Lord our God shall drive out from before us, them will we possess' (Judg. xi. 24).

The kings of the ancient Assyrians were so accustomed to cruelties upon non-Assyrians, and were so proud of these cruelties, that they recorded them in stone as a claim to immortality among men. Assurbanipal, in speaking of the conquered, says : ' I pulled out their tongues and cut off their limbs, and caused them to be eaten by dogs, bears, eagles, vultures, birds of heaven.' Assur-natsir-pal, another wonderful fellow, boasts similarly : ' I flayed the nobles and covered the pyramid with their skins, and their young men and maidens I burned as a holocaust.' ' Their carcasses covered the valleys and the tops of the mountains,' says Tiglath-Pileser in his account of the slain Muskayans ; and Sennacherib informs us proudly that he drove his chariot over the dead bodies of his victims until 'its wheels were clogged with flesh and blood.' 'Evidently,' remarks Spencer, in speaking of these monstrous inscriptions, 'the expectation was that men of after-times would admire these merciless destructions; for we cannot assume that these Assyrian kings intentionally made themselves eternally infamous' (1).

To the ancient Greeks there were two classes of human beings in the world: Greeks and 'barbarians.' The Greeks were the inhabitants of Hellas, which was believed to be the central region of the world, and the 'barbarians' were the godless denizens of the less-favoured and less centrally located remainder of the earth. The world was believed to be flat or shield-shaped, and in its exact centre stood Mount Olympus in northern Thessaly. This mountain, which is 9,700 feet high, was supposed to be the highest elevation on the earth, and was the awful abode of the gods. The Greeks called themselves Hellenes. According to their fabled genealogy, they were the descendants of Hellen, son of Deucalion, the Greek Noah. While they were often at war with each other, they spoke a common language, and always regarded themselves as members of a single family. All non-Greeks were 'barbarians,' including the Romans, who were called 'barbarians' down to the time of Augustus. While the Greeks themselves traced their ancestry back to the bright blood of the gods, the 'barbarians' were generally supposed to have originated from stones and trees. The 'barbarians' were looked upon and treated by the Greeks everywhere as a different order of beings from themselves. Those taken by them in war were regularly reduced to slavery. The slave population created in this way was increased by the slave traffic carried on with the East until the slave population of Greece was several times as great as the free population. The whole Hellenic world, in fact, even in the days of its greatest magnificence, was one vast pen of slaves. Almost every freeman of Attica was a slave-owner. Out of a population of about five hundred thousand, four hundred thousand were slaves. It was considered a real hardship by the Greeks to be compelled to get along with less than a half-dozen slaves. In Corinth and Ægina there were ten slaves to one freeman. In Sparta the slaves were the vanquished Helots, the original inhabitants of the Peloponnesus, whom the Spartans had conquered and reduced to chains in early times. Their lot was particularly horrible. They were the property of the state, and were distributed to the Spartan lords by lot. ' They practically had no rights which their masters felt bound to respect. If one of their number displayed unusual powers of either body or mind, he was secretly assassinated, as it was deemed unsafe to allow such qualities to be fostered in the servile class. It is affirmed [by Thucydides] that, when the Helots grew too numerous for the supposed safety of the state, their numbers were thinned by deliberate massacre of the surplus population ' (4). The conception of human slavery entertained by the common mass of Greeks may be inferred from the fact that philosophers like Aristotle taught that 'slaves were simply domestic animals possessed of intelligence.' It is this fact, this utter lack of justice and humanity manifested by the Greeks in their treatment of non-Hellenic mankind, which gives to Greek 'civilisation' its seamy side. Greek society has been appropriately likened to a pyramid, its apex gleaming with light and splendour, while its base was sunk in darkness.

Non-Romans were called 'barbarians' also by the Romans, and were considered by the Romans to be an entirely different order of beings from themselves. Any splinter of a Roman was, according to the Romans, superior to the most illustrious 'barbarian.' Men were not treated nor estimated according to their intrinsic qualities, but wholly as to whether they were or were not 'Roman citizens.' To be a 'Roman citizen' was to be entitled to everything; to be a 'barbarian' was not to be entitled to anything necessarily, except to serve in some way the all-glorious Romans. The elaborate legal and ethical codes formulated by these masters of the Mediterranean were reserved religiously for themselves. The business of the 'barbarians' was to furnish fields for pillage and conquest, to impart magnitude to triumphal pageants, to act as slaves, and to die by ignominiously butchering each other for the amusement of their bloodthirsty masters. 'Barbarian' lands were looked upon simply as game-preserves where ambitious captains from the Tiber went to refresh their reputations by hunting and victimising the inhabitants. The history of Rome is the history of infamy on a colossal, almost world-wide, scale. There has never been displayed by any people pretending to be civilised such shameless savagery as that displayed by the Romans in their gladiatorial arenas, where men (generally the captives of war) were 'butchered to make a Roman holiday.' These tragedies, in their magnitude and atrocity, seem almost frightful when we read of them on the pages of history. They were generally celebrated by victorious captains and emperors at the close of some unusual outrage against the 'barbarians,' or upon the departure of Roman legions for the field of activity. The celebrations sometimes lasted weeks, or even months. The Emperor Trajan celebrated his victories over the Dacians with shows that lasted more than a hundred days. During this horrible festival ten thousand men fought upon the arena, and more than ten thousand wild animals were slain. The gladiators in these ancient combats fought in chariots, on horseback, on foot—in all the ways in which soldiers fought in actual battle. They fought with swords, lances, daggers, tridents, and every other manner of weapon. Some had nets and lassoes with which they entangled their adversaries, and then slew them. The life of a wounded gladiator was in the hands of the spectators, who showed their clemency or their lack of it by turning their thumbs respectively down or up. The thirst of the populace for blood

was sometimes such that the dying were aroused
and forced on to the fight by burning with a
hot iron. The dead bodies were dragged from
the arena with hooks, like the carcasses of
animals, and the pools of blood soaked up with
dry sand (5). There was an occasional Roman,
like Seneca, sane enough to realise the real character of these performances, and brave enough
to denounce them as crimes. But by the great
mass of all classes of Romans, even by those who
pretended to think, they were regarded with perfect moral indifference. The excuse offered by
Pliny was generally concurred in by his countrymen, that these bloody shows were necessary for
the cultivation of manliness and for keeping
awake the strenuous and red-handed instincts in
the young.

Scarce less revolting than the gladiatorial arena,
in its violation of every principle of humanity,
was the institution of human slavery. During the
later republic and the earlier empire, one-half
the population of the Roman state was slaves.
The slave population was recruited chiefly, as in
Greece, by war and by slave-hunting. Slave-
traders and slave-markets flourished both in the
capital itself and in all the great ports visited by
Roman ships. Some of the outlying provinces of
Asia and Africa were almost depopulated by the
slave-hunters. Greek slaves were the highest-
priced, because the most intelligent. Among the
wealthy, who, like the illiterate rich of every age,
dawdled their time in ostentation, there were

slaves for each different function in the household. There were the *cubicularii*, who acted as housemaids; the *triclinarii*, who waited at table; the *culinarii*, who acted as kitchen drudges; and the *balnearii*, who looked after the baths. Then there were *tonsores*, or barbers; *criniflores*, or hair-crimpers; *calceatores*, who took care of the feet; and *lectores*, whose business it was to read aloud to their masters at meals, in the bath, or in bed. The *ostiarius*, who was sometimes chained in the vestibule like a dog, was the porter; the *invitator* summoned the guests; and the *servus ab hospitiis* looked after their lodgment. There was the slave called the *sandalio*, whose sole duty was to care for his master's sandals; and another, called the *nomenclator*, whose exclusive business it was to accompany his master when he went upon the street, and give him the names of such persons as he ought to recognise. The common punishment for a refractory slave was beating. If the runaway were caught, as he could hardly fail to be, since there were extremely heavy penalties for harbouring or assisting him, he was either branded or had an iron collar like a dog's welded around his neck, or his legs were fettered, or, in exaggerated or repeated cases of offence, he was at once turned into the arena or otherwise put to death. If he attempted to take personal vengeance upon his master for any wrong whatsoever, his whole family shared his fate, and the regular form of capital punishment for a slave was crucifixion under the most ignominious and agonising circumstances (6).

' In many cases, as a measure of precaution, the slaves were forced to work in chains and to sleep in subterranean prisons. The feeling entertained toward this unfortunate class in the later republican period is illustrated by Varro's classification of slaves as " vocal agricultural implements," and by Cato the Elder's recommendation that old and worn-out slaves be sold, as a matter of economy. Sick and hopelessly infirm slaves were taken to an island in the Tiber, and there left to die of starvation and exposure' (5). Slaves were practically without any rights whatever to the world in which they lived. A Roman could take the life of his Gallic slave with as complete impunity as an American can slay his bovine servant to-day. Romans, in short, looked upon and treated non-Romans about as human beings to-day look upon and treat non-humans—as *mere prey*.

V. Modern Ethics.

But the peoples of the ancient world are not the only human beings who have suffered from the psychological bequests of savages. Modern states and peoples, notwithstanding their far-flung professions of righteousness, manifest, though in a somewhat weakened form, the same ethnic prejudices and the same senseless antipathies as those displayed by the ancients. Remnants of the primitive tribal morality are found in the moral habits and conceptions of every people, however emancipated they may imagine themselves to be. Many a person who would not think of swindling one of his neighbours will not hesitate to swindle a foreigner, especially if the foreigner happens to be of a nationality much removed in language, colour, manners, or interests from his own. Morality is genetic. It is not a consistent something—something reasoned out and framed according to the facts. It has grown up. It is essentially tribal—whether it is confined to a family, as is done by some, to a corporation or trade, to a nation, to an artificial fraternity, or to a species. We are, in fact, all of us, even the broadest and most illuminated, simply savages more or less leafed out. We all suffer, as men have always suffered, from the over-vividness of the presentative powers of the mind (sensation and perception) compared with the representative powers (memory and imagination). We all exaggerate out of their proper perspective in the phenomena of a universe the things that are around us and about us—the events we witness or take part in, the things that are ours, and the affairs of the street, city, state, neighbourhood, world, and time, in which we live. Every human being (the sage less than the savage, but the sage to some extent) is inclined to lump together as foreign to him, and as more or less useless and shadowy in themselves, the things, beings, and events that are distant, and to consider them of less reality than those with which he is directly concerned, and of which his knowledge is immediate. *The evolution of consciousness in its social and ethical aspects consists in the evolution of the ability to make real and vivid the phenomena that are more and more distant in both space and time.*

The Chinese call their country 'the flower of the middle,' and believe it to be the central and choicest portion of the earth's surface. All those beyond the bounds of ' The Heavenly Flower Kingdom' are, by those on the inside, venomously lumped together as 'foreign devils.' The people of Spain look upon themselves in much the same way as the Chinese look upon themselves, although they are in reality the most belated of all peoples to-day pretending to be civilised. There are a few travelled and educated Spaniards who realise the pitiful place held by their country in the family of reputable states. ' But the great mass of the people are not only perfectly satisfied with their condition, but consider themselves the most fortunate of all God's creatures. They never go outside of their country and never read a foreign newspaper or book. Like the Chinese, they consider other nations barbarians, and point to Madrid as the centre of civilisation.' The French, down to the nineteenth century, confiscated the property of all aliens who died within the realm ; and the savage practice of punishing one alien for the crimes of another alien was sanctioned by the laws of England down to the middle of the fourteenth century. It has been only a day in the history of the world since Caucasians hunted their dusky brothers in Africa like 'wild animals,' and sold and loaned and lashed them as we do horses to-day. Men now living can remember when it made no difference how exalted in character men might be: if a certain pigment of their bodies was dark, they were ' niggers.' They had no ' souls' as pale men had, and no more chance of paradise than cattle. At the beginning of the nineteenth century, incredible as it may seem, every country of Europe and America held slaves, and was engaged in the soulless avocation of man-hunting in Africa. Tens of thousands of Africa's children were annually seized by prowling pirate bands and exported to distant lands to wear their lives out in disgrace and drudgery. It was not until the latter part of the nineteenth century that civilised nations, following the initiative of England, finally abolished human slavery, the United States and Brazil being the last to act. The Christian sneers at all who do not bow down to his deities and worship according to his ritual, as ' heathens' or ' freethinkers,' and to the Moslem all who are not followers of 'the True Prophet' are ' infidel dogs.' The history of these two religions is a chronicle of almost unparalleled crimes upon disbelievers.

But it is not necessary to go to Arabia or Cathay, nor even necessary to read history, in order to find examples of bigotry and provincialism. It is only necessary to open our eyes. Americans are not a peculiar people—unless it be in the unbridled character of their conceit. All the barbarism is not behind us nor around us. History looks dark and discouraging to us, as we turn its terrible pages, but we would see something just as discouraging if we would look into a mirror. The old savage spirit still circulates in our veins. The 'foreigner' is not an enemy, but he is still an individual whose chief significance is in his 'fleece.' If the 'foreigner' did not ease our economic theories by benevolently 'paying the tax,' it would be hard to tell what would become of him. Those who suffer from a different government, speak a different language, or laud other gods are regarded by us as distinctly inferior to ourselves. Millions of dollars are annually squandered by self-righteous societies in sending missionaries to the other side of the planet to peoples who need evangels of mercy and humanity far less than we do ourselves. In these times of ecclesiastical enterprise, however, missionaries are being superseded, as agents of evangelisation, by the more effective inventions of Messrs. Maxim and Krupp. 'American' is regarded by us as the synonym of perfection, and to be 'patriotic' is to give unthinking enthusiasm to every scheme incubated by wolfish spoilsmen. Crimes of conquest carried on by others become, when undertaken by us, shining masterpieces of 'benevolent assimilation.' We are not so far from the naked and unkempt contemporaries of the cave-bear and sabre-toothed lion as we imagine we are. To carry a bayonet, and especially to redden it with an alien's blood, is here in this degenerate land of Jefferson, more glorious than to create a book. Captains particularly competent as butchers, though their characters be as coarse as a savage chief's, are hailed as heroes by thousands besides silly women, and held up, like the cut-throats of the Kukis, as the highest exemplars of right-doing. Old Rameses, holding by their hair a half-dozen dwarfs, and ostentatiously cutting off their heads with a single sweep of his sword, finds his modern counterpart in miserable Americans pompously gloating over the offhand slaughter of the children of distant archipelagoes.

VI. The Ethics of Human Beings toward Non-Human Beings.

But the most mournful instance of provincial ethics afforded by the inhabitants of the earth is not that furnished by the varieties of the human species in their conduct toward each other, but that afforded by the human race as a whole in its treatment of the non-human races. Human nature is nowhere so hideous, and human con-science is nowhere so profoundly inoperative, as in their disregard for the life and happiness of the non-human animal world. With the develop-ment of the representative powers of the mind, the widening and mutualising of human activities, and the consequent enlargement of the human horizon, the feeling of amity has spread and intensified, until to-day, notwithstanding all that is true of human sectionalism, the ethical systems of civilised peoples include, theoretically at least, and more or less seriously, all human beings whatsoever. Ethical consciousness has extended from individual to family, from family to clan, from clan to tribe, from tribe to confederacy, from confederacy to kingdom, from kingdom to race, from race to species, until, in the case of many millions of men, ethical feeling has reached, with greater or less vividness and consistency, the anthropocentric stage of evolution. The fact that an individual is a *man*—that is, that he belongs to the human species of animals—entitles him in all civilised lands to the fundamental rights and privileges of existence. The rights to life, liberty, and the pursuit of happiness are believed to-day, by all exalted minds, to be the inalienable properties of every *human* being who comes into the world.

But, except by occasional individuals here and there whose emotions are more civilised than the rest, or whose conceptions are more ample and clear, ethical relations are not extended by human beings beyond the bounds of their own species. Non-human millions are *outsiders*. They are looked upon and treated by human beings as if they were an entirely different order of existences, with entirely different purposes and susceptibilities, from human beings. They are not considered to be living beings at all, as human beings are, who are here in the world to enjoy life and all that life holds that is dear to a living being. They belong to the same class of existences as the waves of the sea and the weeds of the field. They are looked upon as mere *things* — mere moving, multiplying objects, without the slightest equity in the world in which they find themselves. They may be set upon, beaten, maimed, starved, assassinated, eaten, insulted, deceived, imprisoned, robbed, tormented, skinned alive, shot down for pastime, cut to pieces out of curiosity, or compelled to undergo any other enormity or victimisation anybody can think of or is disposed to visit upon them. It is enough almost to make knaves shudder, the cold-blooded and business-like manner in which we cut their throats, dash out their brains, and discuss their flavour at our cannibalistic feasts. As Plutarch says, 'Lions, tigers, and serpents we call savage and ferocious, yet we ourselves come behind them in no species of barbarity.' Accustomed from our cradle up to look upon violence and assassination, we have become so habituated and hardened to these things that we perpetrate them and see them perpetrated with the same indifference as that with which we watch waves die on the beach. Human beings are, in fact ('paragons' though they pretend to be), the most predatory and brutal of all animals —the great bone-breakers and bone-pickers of the planet.

It is scarcely possible, astounding as it is, to commit crimes upon any beings in this world, except men. There *are* no beings in the universe, according to human beings, except themselves. All others are *commodities*. They are of consesequence only because they have thighs and can fill up the unoccupied places of the human alimentary. Human beings are 'persons,' and have souls and gods and places to go to when they die. But the hundreds of thousands of other races of terrestrial inhabitants are mere 'animals,' mere 'brutes,' and 'beasts of the field,' 'livestock' and 'vermin.' Every crime capable of being perpetrated by one being upon another is day after day rained upon them, and with an equanimity that would do honour to the managers of an inferno. Human beings preach as the cardinal rule of morality — and they seem never to tire of its reiteration—that they should do unto others as they would that others would do unto them; but they hypocritically confine its application to the members of their own crowd, notwithstanding there are the same reasons identically for extending it to all creatures. The happiness of the human species is assumed to be so much more precious than that of others that the most sacred interests of others are unhesitatingly sacrificed in order that human desires may all be fastidiously catered to. Even for a tooth or a feather or a piece of skin to wear on human vanity, forests are depopulated and the land filled with the dead and dying. Assassination is the commonest and most fashionable of human pastimes. Jaded systems are regularly recuperated by massacre. Men arm themselves—men who roar about 'rights,' and even ministers of mercy—and go out on killing expeditions with as little compunction as savages put on war-paint. They come back from their campaigns of crime like the cut-throats of old Rome, trailing their victims as trophies, and expecting to be hailed as heroes for the hells they have established. Barbarians preponderate, and morality is turned inside out. Cruelty is lionised, and broad-mindedness is rewarded with a sneer. Compassion is a disease, and to be fashionable is to be a fiend. If non-human peoples had no nerves and no choice of emotions, and were utterly indifferent to life, they could scarcely be treated more completely as personal nonentities.

The denial by human animals of ethical relations to the rest of the animal world is a phenomenon not differing either in character or cause from the denial of ethical relations by a tribe, people, or race of human beings to the rest of the human world. The provincialism of Jews toward non-Jews, of Greeks toward non-Greeks, of Romans toward non-Romans, of Moslems toward non-Moslems, and of Caucasians toward non-Caucasians, is not one thing, and the provincialism of human beings toward non-human beings another. They are all manifestations of the same thing. The fact that these various acts are performed *by* different individuals and *upon* different individuals, and are performed at different times and places, does not invalidate the essential sameness of their natures. Crimes are not classified (except by savages or their immediate derivatives) according to the similarity of those who do them or those who suffer from them, but by grouping them according to the similarity of their intrinsic qualities. All acts of provincialism consist essentially in the disinclination or inability to be universal, and they belong in reality, all of them, to the same species of conduct. There is, in fact, but one great crime in the universe, and most of the instances of terrestrial wrong-doing are instances of this crime. It is the crime of *exploitation*—the considering by some beings of themselves as *ends*, and of others as their *means*—the refusal to recognise the equal, or the approximately equal, rights of all to life and its legitimate rewards—the crime of acting toward others as one would that others would *not* act toward him. For millions of years, almost ever since life began, this crime has been committed, in every nook and quarter of the inhabited globe.

Every being is an *end*. In other words, every being is to be taken into account in determining the ends of conduct. This is the only consistent outcome of the ethical process which is in course of evolution on the earth. This world was not made and presented to any particular clique for its exclusive use or enjoyment. The earth belongs, if it belongs to anybody, to the beings who inhabit it—to *all* of them. And when one being or set of beings sets itself up as the sole end for which the universe exists, and looks upon and acts toward others as mere means to this end, it is usurpation, nothing else and never can be anything else, it matters not by whom or upon whom the usurpation is practised. A tyrant who puts his own welfare and aggrandisement in the place of the welfare of a people, and compels the whole people to act as a means to his own personal ends, is not more certainly a usurper than is a species or variety which puts its welfare in the place of the welfare of all the inhabitants of a world. The refusal to put one's self in the place of others and to act toward them as one would that they would act toward him does not depend for its wrongfulness upon who makes the refusal or upon whether the refusal falls upon this or that individual or set. Deeds are right and wrong in themselves; and whether they are right or wrong, good or evil, proper or improper, whether they should be done or should not be done, *depends upon their effects upon the welfare of the inhabitants of the universe.* The basic mistake that has ever been made in this egoistic world in the judging and classifying of acts has been the mistake of judging and classifying them with reference to their effects upon some particular fraction of the inhabitants of the universe. In pure egoism conduct is judged as good or bad solely with reference to the results, immediate or remote, which that conduct produces, or is calculated to produce, on the *self*. To the savage, that is right or wrong which affects favourably or unfavourably *himself* or his *tribe*. And this sectional spirit of the savage has, as has been shown, characterised the moral conceptions of the peoples of all times. The practice human beings have to-day—the practice of those (relatively) broad and emancipated minds who are large enough to rise above the petty prejudices and 'patriotisms' of the races and corporations of men, and are able to view 'the world as their country' (the world of *human* beings, of course)—the practice such minds have of estimating conduct solely with reference to its effects upon the human species of animals is a practice which, while infinitely broader and more nearly ultimate than that of the savage, belongs logically in the same category with it. The partially emancipated human being who extends his moral sentiments to all the members of his own species, but denies to all other species the justice and humanity he accords to his own, is making on a larger scale the same ethical mess of it as the savage. The only consistent attitude, since Darwin established the unity of life (and the attitude we shall assume, if we ever become really civilised), is the attitude of *universal gentleness and humanity*.

'The world is my country,' said Thomas Paine, and every man, woman, and child capable of appreciating the exalted sentiment applauded. But 'the world' of the great freethinker was inhabited by *men only*.

The following lines were written by Robert Whitaker, and first printed in a San Francisco newspaper:

'My Country is the world ! I count
　　No son of man my foe,
Whether the warm life currents mount
　　And mantle brows like snow,
Or whether yellow, brown, or black,
The face that into mine looks back.

'My Native Land is Mother Earth,
　　And all men are my kin,
Whether of rude or gentle birth,
　　However steeped in sin ;
Or rich or poor, or great or small,
I count them brothers one and all.

'My Flag is the star-spangled sky,
  Woven without a seam,
Where dawn and sunset colours lie,
  Fair as an angel's dream,
The Flag that still unstained, untorn,
Floats over all of mortal born.

'My Party is all humankind,
  My Platform, brotherhood;
I count all men of honest mind
  Who work for human good,
And for the hope that gleams afar,
My comrades in the holy war.

'My Country is the world! I scorn
  No lesser love than mine,
But calmly wait that happy morn
  When all shall own this sign,
And love of country, as of clan,
Shall yield to love of Man.'

Robert Whitaker, you are a grand improvement on the 'jingo.' But you are still too small. There are conceptions as much more prophetic and exalted than yours as your conception is superior to that of the Figian.

Broad as he is who can look upon all men as his brethren and countrymen—broad as he is compared with those groundlings called 'patriots,' who can see nothing clearly beyond the bounds of the political unit to which they belong—he is not broad enough. He is still a *sectionalist*, a *partialist*. He represents but a *stage* in the process of ethical expansion. He is, in fact, small compared with the *universalist*, just as the savage is small compared with the philanthropist. 'Mankind,'

'humanity,' 'all men,' 'the whole human family'
—these are big conceptions, too big for the poor
little nubbins of brains with which most millions
make the effort to think. But they are pitifully
small compared with that grand conception of
kinship which takes in all the races that live and
move upon the earth. Smaller yet are these
conceptions compared with that sublime and
supreme synthesis which embraces not only the
present generation of terrestrial inhabitants, but
which extends longitudinally as well as laterally,
extends in time as well as in space, and embraces
the generations which shall grow out of the existing generation and which are yet unborn—*that
conception which recognises earth-life as a single
process, world-wide and immortal, every part related
and akin to every other part, and each generation
linked to an unending posterity.*

Every individual, therefore, emancipated enough
to judge of acts of conduct according to their
intrinsic natures and consequences rather than
according to some local or traditional bias, cannot
help knowing that the exploitation of birds and
quadrupeds for human whim or convenience is an
offence against the laws of morality, not different
in kind from the offences denounced in human
laws as robbery and murder. The creophagist
and the hunter exemplify the same somnambulism,
are the authors of the same kind of conduct, and
belong literally in the same category of offenders,
as the cannibal and the slave-driver. To take the
life of an ox for his muscles, or to kill a sheep for

his skin is *murder*, and those who do these things or cause them to be done are *murderers* just as actually as highwaymen are who blow off the heads of hapless wayfarers for their guineas. If these things *seem untrue*, it is not because they *are* untrue, but because those to whom they seem so *are unable to judge conduct from the quadrupedal point of view*. If there were in this world beings as much more clever than Caucasians as Caucasians are more clever than cows and sheep, and these beings should regard themselves as the darlings of the gods and should attach a fictitious dignity and importance to their own lives, but should look upon Caucasians as simply so much 'beef' and 'mutton,' these bleached terrorists of the world would in the course of a few generations of experience probably become sufficiently illumined to realise that current human conceptions of cows and sheep are not only preposterous, but fiendish.

VII. The Origin of Provincialism.

Human provincialism, all of it, is the consequence of a common cause—*the provincialism of the savage*. Back of the provincialism of the savage is, of course, the antecedent fact of primordial egoism. The savage is the common ancestor of all men, and as such has imparted to all men their general characters of mind and heart. Everything that grows, whether it be a tree, a human being, a grass blade, or a race, grows from something. This something, this germ or embryo from which each thing springs, imparts to the thing its fundamental characters. However far anything may evolve, and however much it may come to differ superficially from its original, it will always remain at heart more or less faithful to the facts of its genesis. This hereditary tendency of everything, this tendency toward invariability, is the conservative, or inertial tendency of the universe. All races, colours, and conditions of men—civilised, slightly civilised, and barbarous—extend back to, and take root in, savages, just as all savages have probably sprung in some still more remote period of the past from a single stirp of anthropoids. The savage is, therefore, the author of human nature and philosophy. Just as the fish, which is the common ancestor of all amphibians, reptiles, birds, and mammals, has predetermined the general structural style of all subsequently evolved vertebrates, so the savage, as the original ancestor of mankind, has predetermined the general mental and dispositional make-up of all higher men. That civilised and semi-civilised men are naturally narrow and revengeful, selfish and superstitious, and find it next to impossible to feel and act toward others as they would like to have others feel and act toward them, is, therefore, not more mysterious than that vertebrates have red blood, two eyes, two pairs of limbs, and a backbone with a bulging brain-box at the hither end of it. Just as the habits, beliefs, and conceptions of the child persist, often but slightly modified, in the full-grown man or woman, so the habits, beliefs, and conceptions, formed by the race in its childhood, continue, under the influence of the same laws of inertia, on into the more mature stages of racial development. Human nature changes with great reluctance, and only in its superficial aspects at that. There are cave-men, men with the primitive ideas and practices of the Stone Age, and men in the pastoral and hunting stages of mankind, in all the highest societies of men. There is scarcely a habit, vice, occupation, amusement, crime, or trait of character, found among men of the past but may be seen still among our contemporaries.

Altruism (other-love) is just as natural as egoism (self-love) is. There is not so much of it in the world as there is of egoism. But that is simply the misfortune of our place of existence. There is no reason why there might not have been as much, or even more, under different conditions. With the same antecedents, nothing can, of course, happen differently from what does happen. But with different antecedents, different causes, the results are bound to be different. Civilised men are not beings of altruism, because they are *not* the *effects* of that kind of *causes*. But there is no reason why there might not be a world—several of them, in fact, or even a universeful—where the inhabitants have never known or heard of such an indelicate thing as of beings preferring themselves to others—where it is as natural for them to act toward each other according to what we call the Golden Rule as it is for us terrestrial heathens to violate it. It is possible to conceive of beings with even too much altruism. The ideal condition is one of balanced egoism and altruism—one in which each thinks as much of others as he does of himself, no more and no less. And if beings were endowed with natures rendering them not only willing but *determined* to act primarily in the interests of others, and this condition of things were universal, there would be about as much discord and strife as if everyone acted in the interest of himself. The Golden Rule among a lot of hypothetical otherists like this would be the opposite of ours, for, instead of emphasising the importance of others as we do, they would need to encourage regard for self. Wouldn't it seem original to live in a world where men were sent to gaol for over-benevolence, and where sermons had to be preached on such texts as, ' Love thyself as thy neighbour '; ' It is more blessed to receive than to give '; ' Avoid doing to yourself that which you do not like when done to others '; ' The Lord loves a cheerful taker '; and the like ?

The persistence with which savage ideas and instincts continue to influence men long after those ideas and instincts have really become anachronistic and vestigial is well illustrated by civilised men and women everywhere. The sun continues to ' rise ' and ' set ' in all civilised lands just as it used to do to the savage, although men have long since learned that it does not do either. Hell, as originally conceived, was an actual sub-terranean region, and heaven was an abode located a few hours' journey above the supposedly flat earth. To-day we continue to say '*up* to heaven,' and '*down* to hell' (never 'down to heaven' and 'up to hell'), and always think of these places as being thus relatively located, although it is extremely doubtful whether any really sane mind continues to believe that hell is on the inside of the earth (or any place else, for that matter), and although *up* means simply away from the centre of the earth, and away from the centre of a ball means literally every possible direction. The theological theories of the origin, nature, and destiny of man and of the universe in general, all of which originated in savage or semi-savage minds, and all of which bear the unmistakable traces of their origin, continue to cling to the minds of the masses of civilised men, notwithstanding the inherent absurdity of these theories, and notwithstanding the fact that their unsoundness is vouched for by the most positive and unanimous assurances from the scientific world. Why should civilised men and women, any of them, be indifferent to the sufferings of others, or find delight in such loathsome avocations as the fishing and hunting of their fellow-creatures? Because their ancestors were savages, and they are not yet sufficiently evolved to be independent of the instincts of their savage sires. There is no other explanation. No human being could enjoy seeing a pack of hounds hunt down and rend to pieces a poor harmless hare—unless he were a savage. No human being could go out to the abodes of the squirrel and quail, and shoot murderous balls into their beautiful bodies for food or fun—unless he were a savage. No human being would lounge all day about the margins of a brook, blind to the beauties of the stream and the glories of forest and sky, in order to thrust brutal hooks into the lips of those whom he deceives, and drag them from their waters to suffocate in the sun—unless he were a savage. No human being would have palaces and parks and yachts and equipages, townships of lands, packs of hounds, and studs of horses, troops of lackeys and nothing to do, when all around him are the men and women who made this wealth, half clad and half starved, suffocating in shanties and working like wretches from morning till night—unless he were a savage. All of these deeds are savage deeds, deeds of exceeding thoughtlessness and brutality, and, instead of being enjoyable, are to every emancipated mind positively painful.

Hunting, fishing, and fighting are the chief occupations of savage life. Back of the activities displayed in these occupations are powerful instincts prompting and sustaining them. Civilised peoples are devoted primarily to the arts of industry and peace. But there are enough savages in every civilised society, and enough of the savage spirit in those who pretend to approximate the civilised state, to give to civilised life a decidedly barbaric aspect. War is a more or less regular exercise, and killing and competing and torturing enter largely into the pastimes of all peoples.

Next to eating, fighting, in one form or another, is the favourite pursuit of men nearly everywhere on holy days and days of leisure. Whenever human beings have any energy or time left over from what they are required to spend in maintaining their existence, they use it in fighting somebody or in watching somebody else fight. And generally the more brutal and sanguinary the conflict, the more popular and satisfying it is. Witness the bull-fights and cock-fights of Spain and Mexico, the fisticuffs of Anglo-Saxons, and the baseball and slugball battles of the Americans, where eager thousands gather and roar for hours like hysterical idiots simply to see one animal or set of animals punish or discredit another. If there are no pigeons to shoot, or if the community is ruled by men and women who are too emancipated to allow such things, we make glass birds and heroically bang away at them, supplying by our imaginations the blood and agony of real carnage. And if we can't do anything else, we take some poor pig, that never did anyone any harm in the world, and grease it and turn it loose, and then take after it with knives, as Chicago butchers do on vacation days, and see who can cut its throat the quickest. This amusement, in pure barbarity, certainly stands pretty near the top in the list of human pastimes so far invented. Maybe it is outclassed by that other contest sometimes advertised as a feature of butchers' barbecues, in which a band of professional cutthroats compete to see who can kill, skin, and eviscerate the largest number of their fellow-beings in a given time.

Games and other performances in which interest is aroused by contending or killing are all of them entertainments gotten up primarily for the amusement of the under-exercised savage within us. The bloody carnivals of the ancient Romans, which seem so incomprehensible to the people of to-day, find their diabolical parallels right here in our high-sniffing civilisation. The bull-pen, where poor quadrupeds are baited by gorgeous assassins for the amusement of Castilian communities, and the cockpit and the prize-ring, where irate fowls and naked thugs peck and pound each other to insensibility for the entertainment of blood-loving mobs, are the legitimate succcessors of the gladiatorial arena of the Romans. The gladiatorial horror is not changed, either in its nature or functions, by changing the combatants to cocks and bulls. The ringside roars that rise to-day beside the Tagus and the Hudson over the fatal thrust of the matador or the knockout lunge of the pugilist are howls of barbaric elation arising from the satisfaction of the same instincts as those which seventeen centuries ago made amphitheatres thunder at the spectacle of gutted Gauls. The ability to enjoy strife and suffering in one form is not different in kind from the ability to be entertained by strife and suffering in any other form. Beings who can follow in riotous glee the terrified form of a fleeing stag, or shout ecstatically at sight of the death-stagger of a mangled ox, are psychologically equipped to go into raptures over the blood-curdling combustions of a literal hell.

Few pastimes indulged in by civilised peoples are more horrible to an emancipated mind than that of bull-fighting. It is the national amusement of Spain, and is carried on among all peoples who have acquired their natures and institutions from the Spanish. 'Every Sunday afternoon, whenever the weather permits, 14,000 or 15,000 men and women, representing every class of society, mothers and grandmothers, priests and monks, assemble at the Plaza de Toros in Madrid to witness the most brutal spectacle the human taste approves. Six bulls are tortured and worried until they are exhausted. Then they are killed by the thrusts of the sword of a matador, who is the most popular person in the community and makes more money than any other man. Often as many as twelve horses are ripped open by the horns of the infuriated bulls, and are allowed to die in the presence of the audience, with blood gushing from their wounds and their entrails dragging upon the ground. This sort of thing is carried on not only in Madrid, but is a regular weekly festival in all the cities of Spain. The horses are blindfolded, so they cannot even see what attacks them. The men who torture the bulls have wooden screens behind which they can dodge when pursued, and if one of the baited creatures crowds too closely upon any of its tormentors, the other matadors throw a blanket over its head. It is not sport, for the poor bulls have no chance whatever to escape or to fight back. It is simply slow butchery, an exhibition of unmitigated cowardice and cruelty. And yet, although the Spanish people are the most religious people of Europe, 95 per cent. of the population approve this atrocious barbarism—not only approve it, but demand that the King shall appear in the royal box at every bull-fight, or have his throne upset.'

The notorious 'Juke' family of criminals, who sprang from a single ruffian who lived in 1720, has cost the State of New York millions of dollars in money and incalculable misery and crime. But the initial savage progenitors of the human species have stocked the earth with the most stupendous array of wrong-doers — knaves, felons, kings, warriors, barbarians, butchers, brutalitarians, kleptomaniacs, and thugs —that has ever (let us hope) brought damnation to a world.

VIII. Universal Ethics.

There are the same reasons for the recognition by human beings of ethical relations to non-human beings as there are for the recognition by human beings of ethical relations among themselves. Analyse the reasons for being considerate toward men, any variety of men, and you will find the same reasons to exist for being considerate toward all men. And analyse the reasons for being altruistic toward men — for being kind and sympathetic toward them—and you will find the same reasons to exist for being altruistic toward those who are not men. The doctrine that we human beings may perform upon the other inhabitants of the earth all sorts of injurious acts, and that these acts when so performed by us are perfectly right and proper, but that these same things when done by others to us are crimes, is the logic of pure brutalitarianism. It is a doctrine utterly without intelligence, at variance with every sentiment of justice and humanity, and has no legitimate existence outside the fibrous brains of ruffians.

Right and *wrong* are qualities belonging to two diverse kinds of conduct. They are the qualities which render conduct respectively proper and improper. All terrestrial races (unless the very lowest) have the power of experiencing two kinds of conscious states—the desirable (pleasurable) and the undesirable (painful). Now, if beings were indifferent as to what sort of conscious states entered into and made up their experiences, there would manifestly be no such thing as propriety and impropriety in the causing of these states. But they are not indifferent. The pleasurable experiences are the experiences all beings are seeking, and the painful ones are the ones they are all seeking to avoid. Those acts which help or tend to help beings to those experiences for which they are striving are, therefore, right and proper, and are, they and their authors, called *good.* While those acts which compel beings to undergo that which they are striving to avoid are improper and wrong, and are, they and their authors, called *bad*. Kindness, courtesy, justice, mercy, generosity, sympathy, love, and the like, are good, and selfishness, cruelty, deceit, pillage, injustice, and murder, are bad, because they are respectively the promoters and destroyers of well-being and happiness in the world.

But these two kinds of conduct produce the same respective effects upon non-human beings as they do upon human beings. The emotion of a mangled sensory—is it not the same terrible thing whether the sensory hang to the brain of a quadruped or a man? Do shelter and food not affect shivering and empty cattle, horses, and fowls, precisely as they do human beings? Thunder harsh words at your dog. Will he not shrink and suffer, just as your child or hired hand will under like acts of terrorisation? Speak kindly to him, love him, and accord to him a quarter of the consideration you claim for yourself. Is he not caused to be one of the happiest and most devoted of associates? To take squirrels or song-birds, the most active of animals, and shut them up in narrow cages, and keep them there shut off from their companions and their own green world their whole lives long; to take an animal as sensitive and high-minded as the horse and put a pack on his back and a bit in his mouth, and then strike him dozens of times a day with a lash whose touch is like fire; to shoot off the legs and wings of birds and fill their vitals with lead, and leave them to flounder out a lingering death in the reeds and grasses—do these things not cause misery and desolation in the world? To place temptations in the way of fur-bearing animals and induce them to enter carefully concealed traps, and then allow them to remain in the villainous clutches of these devices, not minutes, but hours, perhaps days, until it suits the convenience of the ensnarer to knock out their brains, or until, crazed by pain, the poor wretches eat off their own limbs and escape—is not this a *monstrous* thing to do?

Oh that men everywhere were moved by the deep tenderness and the all-embracing sympathy of poor Robert Burns, who could apologise with real feeling to a frightened field-mouse whom he had accidentally upturned with his plough.

> ' Wee, sleekit, cow'rin', tim'rous beastie,
>   O, what a panic's in thy breastie !
>   Thou needna start awa' sae hasty,
>   Wi' bick'ring brattle !
>   I wad be laith to rin and chase thee,
>   Wi' murd'rous pattle !
>
> ' I'm truly sorry man's dominion
>   Has broken nature's social union,
>   And justifies that ill opinion
>   Which makes thee startle
>   At me, thy poor, earth-born companion,
>   And fellow-mortal.'

Long ago it was said, and truthfully, that the merciful man is merciful to his ox. The truly kind man, the truly honest and the truly humane man, is not kind and honest and humane to men only, but to *all* beings—to the humble and lowly as well as to the proud and powerful—*to all that have the misfortune to feel and mourn.* Benevolence

is the same beautiful thing whether it pour sunshine into the dark and saddened souls of men or
into the dark and saddened souls of other beings.
John Howard never hearkened to a nobler duty
when he lifted the darkness that hung over English
gaols than will some inflamed soul some day who
hears the cry of the lonely captives who to-day
languish in menagerial dungeons to satisfy human
curiosity. He who will emancipate horses from
the hell in which they pass their lives—make
them the associates of men instead of their slaves
—will deserve to stand in the constellation of the
world's redeemers beside Garrison and Garibaldi.
Is there he who holds in his heart-cups the love
and compassion of Buddha? Let him go where
the dagger drips and the heartless pole-axe crashes,
and the meek-eyed millions of the meadows pour
out their innocent existences in the soulless houses
of slaughter. Let him lift from off the races the
hounding incubus of fear, give back to them their
birthright—the right to a free, unhunted life—and
make the great monster (man) to be their high-
priest and friend.

> ' Among the noblest in the land,
> Though he may count himself the least,
> That man I honour and revere
> Who, without favour, without fear,
> In the great city dares to stand
> The friend of every friendless beast,
> And tames with his unflinching hand
> The brutes that wear our form and face,
> The were-wolves of the human race.'

If to do good is to generate welfare, then to cause welfare to a horse, a bird, a butterfly, or a fish, is to do good just as truly as to cause welfare to men. And if to do evil is to cause unhappiness and illfare, then to cause these things to one individual or race is evil just as certainly as to cause them to any other individual or race. And if to put one's self in the place of others, and to act toward them as one would wish them to act toward him, is the one great rule—the Golden Rule—by which men are to gauge their conduct when acting toward each other, then this is also the one great rule—the Golden Rule—by which men are to regulate their conduct toward all beings. There is no escape from these conclusions, except for the savage and the fool.*

IX. The Psychology of Altruism.

The growth of altruism in the world has been largely cotemporaneous with the growth of the power of *sympathy*. Sympathy is the emotion a

* The deliberate causing of misery and death to criminals, whether they be human or non-human beings, individuals or species, is not, as is sometimes supposed, a violation or reversal of the general theory of ethics. When they are prompted by a spirit of tenderness and universal goodness rather than by a spirit of revenge, penalties are justifiable by the everyday assumption that it is sometimes wise to inflict or undergo a certain amount of illfare in order to avoid or forestall a larger amount. The problems of universal penology are not different from those of human penology, practically the same cases and perplexities being presented by all delinquents. See 'Better-World Philosophy,' by the author, pp. 218-227, for a discussion of the function of punishment.

being has when by means of his imagination he gets so actually into the place of another that his own feelings duplicate more or less the feelings of that other. It is the ability or the impulse to weep with those who weep, and rejoice with those who are glad. Sympathy is the substance and the only sure basis of morality—the only tie of sincere and lasting mutualism. Men have always been to a considerable extent, and are yet, disposed to think about and act toward each other from motives of mutual fear or advantage. But such motives are not the highest nor the most reliable bonds of fellowship and unity. True altruism and solidarity—true expansion and universalisation of the self—are found in sympathy. It is impossible for one individual to do in his heart to another as he would that another should do to him, unless he is at all times able and willing to get into the place of that other, and to realise in his own consciousness the results to the other of his acts. It is only when there is such an intertwining of the consciousnesses that the joys and sorrows of each individual consist to a greater or less extent of the reflexes of the joys and sorrows around him that there exists true social oneness. The great task of reforming the universe is, therefore, since the world is so steeped in selfishness and hate, the task of endowing beings, or the task of stocking the universe with beings, with dispositions to get out of themselves. If the far-away first parents of men and women had been broad-minded beings instead of narrow—had

been beings whose most natural impulse was to be
kind to others, and whose sympathies were as
far-reaching as feeling—terrestrial life would not
to-day present to the all-seeing understanding the
disheartening spectacle it does present, and the
long struggle for justice and amelioration would
not have been.

The primary fact prompting and underlying the
exploitation of one being or set of beings by
another is, and has always been, *Selfishness.*
Whenever and wherever one people have exploited another—whether the exploiters have been
savages, Jews, Romans, Caucasians, or men—
they have done so primarily because the act of
exploitation was a convenience and pleasure to
them and in harmony with their natures. This
selfishness, in the case of civilised peoples, has
been acquired by them through inheritance from
the savage tribes from whom they have severally
evolved; and the selfishness of the savage is a
legacy from the animal forms from whom the
savage has come. Human selfishness is simply
an eddy of an impulse that is universal—an impulse that has been implanted in the nature of the
life-process of the earth by the manner in which
life has been evolved.

But there is another fact which has generally,
if not always, contributed to every act of exploitation in this world, and that is *Ignorance*—ignorance
on the part of those who have executed the exploitation: not ignorance of grammar or geography
or any other particular branch of human informa-

tion or philosophy, but ignorance regarding those upon whom they have worked their will—unconsciousness on the part of the exploiters of the similarity which actually existed between themselves and their victims. However free an individual may be from naturally selfish impulses, he will never act in an altruistic manner toward others unless he is able to realise that these others, are similar to himself, and that acts toward them produce results of good and evil, of welfare and suffering, similar to what these same acts produce when done to himself. Altruistic conduct implies not only altruistic impulses, but altruistic conceptions as well. Tyrants hold, and have always held, themselves to be an entirely different order of beings from their subjects, and far more deserving. Read history—it is a tale told over and over. Between those who have ruled and those who have served—between the Ends and the Means— has ever yawned a chasm, wide, deep, and impassable. The exploited have always been, according to their masters, a fibrous set, unfavoured and unthought of by the gods, endowed with little feeling or intelligence, and brought into existence more or less expressly as adjuncts to their masters. This is the theory of the savage, and it is the theory of all those who have inherited his narrow and unfeeling philosophy. The Gentile had no rights because he was a 'pagan.' He was a human being, it is true, and had come forth from the womb of woman, just as the Jew had. But he spoke a different language from the Jews, had his own ways of life, belonged to a different order of things, and was irritatingly unconcerned about the gods and traditions of the 'chosen people.' The Gaul had no rights that were inconvenient to Romans, because he was a 'barbarian.' The fact that he had blood, and brains, and nerves, and love of life, and ambitions, and that he suffered when he was subjected to humiliation, hard treatment, and death, just as Romans did, was never really thought of by the arrogant and reckless Romans. Romans never realised in their minds what it meant for non-Romans to be treated as they were treated; and one reason why they never realised it was because it was convenient for them not to do so. To kill or enslave a Gaul or German we now know, who are able to judge these acts from an un-Roman and unprejudiced point of view, was practically the same crime as to kill or enslave a Roman. But it was not so to Romans. The most trifling offence against a Roman citizen was enough, according to Roman law, to condemn the offender to execution. But the most horrible outrages, when committed by Romans upon non-Romans, were nothing. Romans always thought and felt *from the standpoint of Romans.* They never got over into the world of the 'barbarians,' and really pictured to themselves—*really felt*—the misfortunes of their victims. It was the same way with the black man in the eyes of the white man a generation or two ago; it is the same way with the brown man to-day. The black man had no rights that were inconvenient for the white man to respect, because he was a 'nigger,' and had no 'soul,' and was the offspring of Ham. This spirit of unconsciousness, which has been so prominent throughout the history of mankind, still survives in the minds of civilised men and women to-day, as is shown by the conception (or *mis*conception) cherished by the Caucasian toward the 'nigger,' by the Christian toward the 'heathen,' by the Moslem toward the 'infidel,' by the Protestant toward the Catholic, and *vice versâ*, by the plutocrat toward the proletarian, by men toward women, and by the human being toward the 'animal.'

The psychology of the exploitation of non-human beings by human beings is not different in kind from the psychology of any other act of exploitation. The great first cause of man's in-humanity to not-men is the same precisely as the great first cause of man's inhumanity to man—*Selfishness*—blind, brutal, unconscionable egoism. Monopolist-like man thinks and cares only about himself. He has the heart of the bully—deriving from the contemplation of his fiendish supremacy a sort of monstrous satisfaction. But there is also present in this case the same half-sincere, half-fostered nescience as in all other cases of exploitation. The ox, the hare, the bird, and the fish have no rights in the world in which they live other than those that are convenient for men to allow to them, because they are 'animals.' They are assumed to belong to an order of beings entirely different from that to which human beings belong. They are filled with nerves, and brains, and bloodvessels; they love life, and bleed, and struggle, and cry out when their veins are opened, just as human beings do; they have the same general form and structure of body, their bodies are composed of the same organs busied with the same functions; and they are descended from the same ancestors and have been developed in the same world through the operation of the same great laws as we ourselves have. But all of these things, and dozens of others just as significant, are disregarded by us in our hard-hearted determination to exploit them. We have a set of words and phrases which we use in speaking of ourselves, and another very different set for other beings. The very same things are called by different names with wholly different connotations depending on whether it is a man that is referred to or some other being. It is 'murder' to take the life of a human being, but to take the life of a sheep or a cow is only 'knocking it on the head.' A man may murder squirrels or birds all day—that is, he may do that which when done to human beings is called murder—but it is only 'sport' when done to these humble inhabitants of the wilds. The dead body of a man is a 'corpse'; the dead body of a quadruped is only a 'carcass.' A race of horses or dogs is a 'breed'; but a breed of men and women is always respectfully referred to as a race. We perpetuate our blindness by the use of words. We accommodate our consciences by inventing ways of looking at things that will bring out our own lustre and relieve us from the ghastly faces of our crimes. For the human race to rob and kill other races is the same kind of activity exactly as it is for human beings to rob and kill each other. But it is not considered so to-day—except by a few lost-caste ' visionaries ' scattered here and there over Christendom, and some millions of ' heathens ' in Asia.

A short time ago a series of letters came into my hands written from Burmah by an American missionary in that country. According to this writer, one of the greatest obstacles the missionaries have to contend with in their work there is the hostility aroused in the people by the killing and flesh-eating habits of the missionaries themselves. The native inhabitants, who are the most compassionate of mankind, look upon the Christian missionaries, who kill and eat cows and shoot monkeys for pastime, as being little better than cannibals. Contemplate the presumption necessary to cause an individual to leave behind him fields white for mission-work, and travel, at great expense, halfway round the earth in order to preach a narrow, cruel, anthropocentric gospel to a people of so great tenderness and humanity as to be kind even to ' animals ' and enemies !

We human beings feel at liberty to commit any kind of outrage upon other races, and these outrages are looked upon by us as nothing. But the most trifling annoyances of other races are deemed by us of sufficient consequence to justify us in visiting upon them the most fearful retributions.

We can break up the laboriously built home of a mother mouse in the rubbish-heap of our back yard, scatter the pink babies of that mother over the ground to die of cold and starvation, and cause the frightened mother to flee at the risk of her very life—all to give to the terrier and ourselves a little moment of savage pastime. But if that same mother, some hard winter's night, when she has failed in her search elsewhere for something to stay her hunger, comes into our larder and nibbles a bit of cheese or a few mouthfuls of crust from our pie, although she takes but a crumb in all, and is as dainty in her feeding as a lady, we immediately get out our traps and poisons and storm around as if a murder or some other irreparable wrong had been committed. We think of our acts toward non-human peoples, when we think of them at all, *entirely from the human point of view.* We never take the time to put ourselves in the places of our victims. We never take the trouble to get over into their world, and realise what is happening over there as a result of our doings toward them. It is so much more comfortable *not* to do so—*so much more comfortable to be blind and deaf and insane.* We go on quieting our consciences, as best we can, by the fact that everybody else nearly is engaged in the same business as we are, and by the fact that so few ever say anything about the matter—anæsthetised, as it were, by the universality of our iniquities and the infrequency of disquieting reminders.

Many years ago an eccentric but gifted Englishman had a dream in which he saw the fortunes of the world reversed. Man was no longer master, but victim. The earth was ruled by the birds and quadrupeds, the mice and monkeys, who proceeded to inflict upon their erstwhile tyrant the same cruelties he had hitherto inflicted upon them. ' Multitudes of human beings were systematically fattened for the carnivora. They were frequently forwarded to great distances by train, in trucks, without food or water. Large numbers of infants were constantly boiled down to form broth for invalid animals. In over-populous districts babies were given to malicious young cats and dogs to be taken away and drowned. Boys were hunted by terriers and stoned to death by frogs. Mice were a good deal occupied in setting man-traps, baited with toasted cheese, in poor neighbourhoods. Gouty old gentlemen were hitched to night-cabs, and forced to totter, on their weak ankles and diseased joints, to clubs, where fashionable young colts were picked up, and taken, at such speed as whipcord could extract, to visit chestnut fillies. Flying figures in scarlet coats, buckskins, and top-boots were run down by packs of foxes that had nothing else to do. Old cock-grouse strutted out for a morning's sport, and came in to talk of how many brace of country gentlemen they had bagged. Gamekeepers lived a precarious life in holes and caves. They were perpetually harried by game and vermin; held fast in steel traps, their toes were nibbled by stoats and martens; and finally, their eyes picked out by owls and kites, they were gibbeted alive on trees, head downwards, until the termination of their martyrdom. In one especially tragic case, a naturalist in spectacles dodged about painfully among the topmost branches of a wood, while a mias underneath, armed with a gun, inflicted on him dreadful wounds. A veterinary surgeon of Alfort was stretched on his back, his arms and legs secured to posts, in order that a horse might cut him up alive for the benefit of an equine audience; but the generous steed, incapable of vindictive feelings, with one disdainful stamp on the midriff, crushed the wretch's life out' (8).

The following is from the Chinese. The speaker is an ox:

'I request, good people, that you will listen to what I have to say. *In the whole world there is no distress equal to that of the ox.* In spring and summer, autumn and winter, I diligently put forth my strength; during the four seasons there is no respite to my labours. I drag the plough, a thousand-pound weight fastened to my shoulders. Hundreds of thousands of lashes are, by a leather whip, inflicted upon me. Curses and abuses in a thousand forms are poured upon me. I am driven, with threatenings, rapidly along, and not allowed to stand still. Through the dry ground or the deep water I with difficulty drag the plough, with an empty belly; the tears flow from both my eyes. I hope in the morning that I shall be early released, but I am detained until the evening. If, with a hungry stomach, I eat the grass in the middle of the field, the whole family, great and small, insultingly abuse me. I am left to eat any species of herbs among the hills, but you, my master, yourself receive the grain that is sown in the field. Of the *chen paddy* you make rice; of the *no paddy* you make wine. You have cotton, wheat, and herbs of a thousand different kinds. Your garden is full of vegetables. When your men and women marry, amid all your felicity, if there be a want of money, you let me out to others. When pressed for the payment of duties, you devise no plans, but take and sell the ox that ploughs your field. When you see that I am old and weak, you sell me to the butcher to be killed. The butcher conducts me to his home and soon strikes me in the forehead with the head of an iron hatchet, after which I am left to die in the utmost distress. My skin is peeled off, my bones are scraped, and my skin is taken to cover the drum by which the country is alarmed.'

> ' Witness the patient ox, with stripes and yells
> Driven to the slaughter, goaded as he runs
> To madness, while the savage at his heels
> Laughs at the frantic sufferer's fury.'

The angler brags about his 'haul' and the hunter about his 'bag' and his 'big game' with as little realisation of what these things mean as the slave-master boasts of his 'niggers.' Men talk of 'chops' and 'steaks' and 'roasts' with the same somnambulism, the same profound unconsciousness of what these things really signify in the psychic economies of the world, as the conqueror contemplates his 'captives,' the robber his 'spoil,' or the savage his 'scalps.' If before the eyes and in the mind of each individual who sits unconcernedly down to a parsleyed 'steak' could rise the facts in the biography of that 'steak'—the happy heifer on the far western meadows, the fateful day when she is forced by the drover's whip from her home,* the arduous 'drive' to the village and her baffled efforts to escape, the crowding into cars and the long, painful journey, the silent heartaches and the low, pitiful moans, the terrible hunger and thirst and cold, her arrival, bruised and bewildered, in the city, her dazed mingling with others, the great murder-house, the prods and bellowings, the treacherous crash of the brain-axe, the death drop and shudder, the butcher's knife, the gush of blood from her pretty throat, and the glassy gaze of her dead but beautiful eyes—there would be, in spite of the inherent hardness of the human heart, a great drawing back from those acts which render such fearful things necessary. If human beings *could only realise* what the hare suffers, or the stag, when it is pursued by dogs, horses, and men bent on taking its life, or what the fish feels when it is thrust through and flung into suffocating gases,

* I have many times seen cows chased all over their native premises, round and round, through fields and barnyards, across streams and over fences—chased until the poor things were utterly exhausted, and whipped and beaten until their faces and backs were covered with wounds—before they could be compelled to leave for ever the old farm where they had been born and raised.

no one of them, not even the most recreant, could find pleasure in such work. *How painful* to a person of tenderness and enlightenment is *even the thought* of rabbit-shootings, duck-slaughterings, bear-hunts, quail-killing expeditions, tame pigeon massacres, and the like! And yet with what light-hearted enthusiasm the mindless ruffians who do these atrocious things enter upon them! One would think that grown men would be ashamed to arm themselves and go out with horses and hounds and engage in such babyish and unequal contests as sportsmen usually rely on for their peculiar ' glory.' And they would be if grown men were not so often simply able-bodied bullies. *If human beings could only realise what it means to live in a world and associate day after day with other beings more intelligent and powerful than themselves, and yet be regarded by these more intelligent individuals simply as merchandise to be bought and sold, or as targets to be shot at, they would hide their guilty heads in shame and horror.*

The Being from whose breaking heart gushed these lines of sorrow and sympathy on seeing a wounded hare was a god :

' Inhuman man ! curse on thy barbarous art,
   And blasted be thy murder-aiming eye :
   May never pity soothe thee with a sigh,
Nor ever pleasure glad thy cruel heart !

' Go, live, poor wanderer of the wood and field,
   The bitter little that of life remains ;
   No more the thickening brakes and verdant plains
To thee shall home, or food, or pastime yield.

'Seek, mangled one, some place of wonted rest,
    No more of rest, but now thy dying bed ;
    The sheltering rushes whistling o'er thy head,
The cold earth with thy bloody bosom pressed.

'Oft, as by winding Nith I, musing, wait
    The sober eve or hail the cheerful dawn,
    I'll miss thee sporting o'er the dewy lawn,
And curse the ruffian's aim and mourn thy hapless fate.'

We human beings, in our conduct toward the races of beings associated with us on this planet, are almost pure *savages*. We are not even half civilised. And this fact is certain to bring upon us the criticism and condemnation of the more enlightened generations to come. The fact is apparent to-day, however—just as apparent as the barbarity of the Romans—to everyone who will take the trouble to rid himself of the prejudices which enslave and blind him, and view human phenomena from an un-human, extra-terrestrial point of view.

To most persons—to all except to a few—everything is simply a matter of habit and education. And a majority of persons, too, can become educated to one thing about as easily and completely as they can to another. In Mr. Huxley's 'Man's Place in Nature' there is reprinted from an old volume the picture of a butcher's shop as it is said to have existed among the savage Anziques of Africa in the sixteenth century. Mr. Huxley says that the original engraving claims to represent an actual fact, and that he has himself no doubt but it does really stand for just what it purports to represent, especially since the fact has been cor-roborated by Du Chaillu in comparatively recent times. The fact for which this old picture stands is a good illustration of the power of custom in shaping human ideas. In this savage 'market' pretty much the same line of goods appears as is found in modern 'markets,' except that, instead of the quartered corpses of sheep and bullocks, there hang the shoulders, thighs, and gory heads of men. The butcher is represented as standing beside the chopping-block in the act of cutting up the leg of a man. A child's head and other fragments of the human body are piled up on another block, and behind these on pegs are ranged the more pretentious wares of the establish-ment. 'Presently we passed a woman,' says Du Chaillu, in speaking of the cannibalism of the Fans, who were probably identical with those referred to two centuries earlier as Anziques. 'She bore with her a piece of the thigh of a human body, just as we should go to market and carry thence a roast of steak.' We can easily imagine (by the help of the sights we see every day) the anthropophagous crowd standing around giving their early morning orders, and the enter-prising assassin hustling about to wait on them. One of them wants an arm, another wants a leg, another a liver, another a half-dozen nice fat ribs. One fellow wants a tender 'cut' of young girl's sirloin, and another would like an old man's calf for soup. A little naked urchin, who has had to wait a long time in order to get a chance to buy anything at all, exchanges a few shells for a section of human bologna. One fellow wants to know the price of the boy's head which lies on the neighbouring block, and a woman complains that the baby's brains which she bought the day before, and which were recommended as being especially 'fresh and nice,' turned out to be 'bad.' We can see them go home with their gruesome purchases, cook them, and sit down and eat them, discussing their flavour or their lack of it, and remarking their tenderness, toughness, or juiciness, and finally throwing the bones out to the dogs—all with as little thought of the immorality of it as 'Thanksgiving' gluttons have to-day at their feasts of blood. There may have been an occasional 'visionary' among these people fanatical enough to 'refuse to eat meat,' or even to protest against the practice. Probably there was. There generally are a few such discordants in every generation of vipers. But 'fanatics' in those days were in all likelihood, as they are to-day, too few to be troublesome.

To anyone familiar with the pliability of the human conscience, or with the soundness and depth of intellectual sleep, these things are neither impossible nor strange. There is so little looking into the essence of things, so little looking at things as they are, and so much thinking and doing as we are accustomed or told to think and do —there are, in fact, so few who can really think at all—that if we had been accustomed and taught to do so from childhood, and the world were practically unanimous in its conduct and teachings on the matter, very few of us indeed would not sit down to a breakfast of scrambled infant's brains, a luncheon of cold boiled aunt, or a dinner of roast uncle, with as little compunction, perhaps with the same horrible merriment, as we to-day attend a ' barbecue ' or a ' turkey.' Why should we not make hash and sausages out of our broken-down grandfathers and grandmothers just as we do out of our worn-out horses, and help out the pigeons at our killing carnivals with a few live peasants? How much more artistic and civilised to pile our tables on holy days with the gold and crimson of the fields and orchards than to load them with the dead! And yet how strangely few are mature enough to care anything at all about the matter!

Oh, the helplessness and irresponsibility of the human mind! There is no spontaneity, no originality, only the dead level of the machine. How impossible it is for us to think, to discover anything unassisted, to perceive anything after it has been pointed out to us even, if it is a little different from what we are used to! This, it seems to me, is one of the most pathetic things in all this world —this illimitable impotence, this powerlessness to inspect things from any other point of view than the one we inherit when we come into the world; to be a knave or lunatic (or the next thing to it), and never have the slightest suspicion of the fact. The human mind will certainly not always be this way. It will surely be different some time. It seems incredible that the planet will drag along in disgrace this way forever. The men of Europe and America are not so primitive as the junglemen, and the junglemen are superior in some respects to the quadrupeds and reptiles, and this gives reason for a little hope. But *when*, that is the question, *when will it be ? In what distant time will the Golden Dream of our prophetic hours come to this poor darkened larva of a world ?* Ages upon ages after our little existences have gone out, and the detritus of our wasted bodies has wandered long in the labyrinths of the sod or been sown by aimless gusts over our native hills.

X. Anthropocentric Ethics.

Anthropocentricism, which drifted down as a tradition from ancient times, and which for centuries shaped the theories of the Western world, but whose respectability among thinking people has now nearly passed away, was, perhaps, the boldest and most revolting expression of human provincialism and conceit ever formulated by any people. It was the doctrine that man was the centre about whom revolved all facts and interests whatsoever; and Judaism and its two children, Christianity and Mahometanism, were responsible for it. Everything, according to this conception, was interpreted in terms of human utility. Everything was made for man—including women. The sun and moon were luminaries, not worlds, hung there by the fatherly manufacturer of things for

the convenience and delight of his children.   The
stars were perforations in the overarching concave
through which eavesdropping prophets peered into
celestial secrets, and errand-angels came and went
with messages between gods and men.   Not only
the spheres in space, but the earth and all it
contained—the rivers, seas, and seasons, all the
plants that grow, and all the flowers that blow,
and all the millions that swim and suffer in the
waters and skies—were, according to this remorseless notion, the soulless adjuncts of man.   In-
trinsically they were meaningless.   They had significance only as they served the human species.
The hues and perfumes of flowers, the songs of
birds, the dews, the breezes, the rains, the rocks,
the ' beasts of the field and the fowls of the air,'
the great forests, the mighty mountains, the
fearful solitudes, even famine and pestilence, were
all made for the being with the reinless imagination.
Luther believed that the fly—festive little *Musca
domestica,* who inhabits our homes, and sometimes
unwittingly wanders over our tender places—was
a pestiferous invention of the devil, maliciously
sent to annoy him in his meditations.   Garlic
grew on the swamp brim as a handy antidote for
human malaria.   Fruits ripened in the summer-
time because the acids and juices which they
contained were believed to be necessary for man's
health and refreshment.   The great muscles of
the ox were made to provide men with delicacies
and leisure.   The cloak of the ewe was made
without any special thought, or without any

thought at all, of the comforts of the ewe. It
was placed there on the ewe by an all-tender
creator, to be torn by his images from her
bleeding back and worn. The fossil forms found
in the rocks were not the *bonâ fide* remains of
creatures that had lived and perished when the
calcareous foundations of the continents were
forming in ancient sea-beds. They were counter-
feits, slyly designed by a suspicious providence,
and sandwiched among the strata ' to test human
faith.' The rainbow was a phenomenon with
which the laws of reflection and refraction had
nothing whatever to do. It was a sign or seal
stamped on the retreating storms as a pledge that
submersion would not be again used as a punishment for sinners. The universal ruler was conceived to be an individual of transcendent power
and respectability, but was supposed to spend
the most of his time and a good deal of anxiety
on the regulation and repair of his illustrious
likenesses.

The history of intellectual evolution is the
history of disillusionment. The stars, we now
know, are not hatchways, but worlds. They burn
because they are fire. They blaze and circle in
obedience to their own unchangeable inertias, just
as the earth does. They blazed and wheeled when
the elemental matters of the earth mingled indis-
tinguishably with the vapours of the sun, and they
will blaze and wheel when the last inhabitant of
this clod has dissolved into the everlasting atoms.
The earth is not the capital of cosmos nor the

subject of celestial anxiety. The earth is a satrap of the sun—a subordinate among servants, not a sovereign with a retinue of stars. The earth and its contents were not made for man. They were not made at all. They were evolved. The concaves of the sea have been hollowed, the mountains upheaved, and the continents planted and peopled, by the same tendencies as those that hold the universes in their grasp. The primal matters of the earth came out of the substance of the sun, and by the play and activity of these elements and the play and activity of their derivatives were evolved all the multitudinous forms of land, fluid, plant, animal, and society. The flowers that 'blush unseen' do not necessarily 'waste their sweetness on the desert air,' as the poet so melodiously imagines. The colours and scents of flowers serve their purposes—which are to secure the services of insects in fertilisation—quite as well when unperceived, as when perceived by human senses. The non-human races of beings were not made for human beings. They were evolved—the higher forms from the lower forms, and the lower forms from still lower—just as the higher societies of men have been evolved, under the eye of history, out of barbarism and savagery. They are our ancestors. They have made human life and civilisation possible. They made their homes on primeval land patches when the continents we creep over were sleeping in the seas. They lived and loved and suffered and died in order that a being intelligent enough to analyse himself and recreant enough to pick their bones might come into the world.

There are supposed to be something like a million (maybe there are several million) species of inhabitants living on the earth. The human species is one of these. Not more than a few thousand of these species are seriously advantageous to men. The harmful and useless species are many times more numerous than the helpful. Now, if the 999,999 non-human species were made for the human species, why were the hundreds of thousands of species made that are of no possible human importance, and the hundreds of thousands of other species that are a positive injury ? And if by some miraculous stretch of imagination the 999,999 species now living on the earth are conceived to have been made for man, why were the 10,000,000 or 15,000,000 of species made that lived and passed away before there was a human being in existence. Perhaps the traditionist will say— accustomed as he is to treat syllogisms with contempt—that they were made to invigorate human ' faith.'

If the age of the human species be estimated at 50,000 years and the age of the life-process at 100,000,000 years, the time during which man has been on the earth is, when compared with the entire period during which the planet has been tenanted, as 1 to 2,000. And the time during which the earth has been inhabited — immense as that time is when compared with the little span of human history—is also insignificant when compared with the enormous lapse of time during which the planet was slowly cooling and solidifying preliminary to the existence of life. And the entire life of the planet—inconceivably vast as it is—is as nothing compared with that eternity, that duration without beginning or close, during which the sidereal millions have undergone, and are destined to continue to undergo, their countless and immeasurable transformations.

It is about as profound to suppose that the earth and its contents, and the suns, stars, and systems of space, were all made for a single species inhabitating an obscure ball located in a remote quarter of the universe as it is to suppose that the gigantic body of the elephant was made for the wisp of hair on the tip of its tail. *Man* is *not* the *end*, he is but an *incident*, of the infinite elaborations of Time and Space.

XI. Ethical Implications of Evolution.

The doctrine of organic evolution, which forever established the common genesis of all animals, sealed the doom of anthropocentricism. Whatever the inhabitants of this world were or were thought to be before the publication of ' The Origin of Species,' they never could be anything since then but a *family*. The doctrine of evolution is probably the most important revelation that has come to the world since the illuminations of Galileo and Copernicus. The authors of the Copernican theory enlarged and corrected human understanding by disclosing to man the compara-

tive littleness of his world—by discovering that
the earth, which had up to that time been supposed to be the centre and capital of cosmos, is
in reality a satellite of the sun. This heliocentric
discovery was hard on human conceit, for it was the
first broad hint man had thus far received of his true
dimensions. The doctrine of evolution has had,
and is having, and is destined to continue to have,
a similarly correcting effect on the naturally narrow
conceptions of men. It tends to fry the conceit
out of us. It has been impossible since Darwin
for any sane and honest man to go around brag-
ging about having been ' made in the image of his
maker,' or to successfully lay claim to a more
honourable origin than the rest of the creatures of
the earth. And if men had accepted the logical
consequences of Darwin's teachings, the world
would not to-day—a half-century after his revelation—be filled with practices which find their
only support and justification in out-of-date
traditions. But logical consequences, as Huxley
observes, are the official scarecrows of that large
and prolific class of defectives usually known as
fools. The doctrine of evolution is accepted in
one form or another by practically all who think.
It is taught even in school primers. But while
the *biology* of evolution is scarcely any longer
questioned, the *psychology* and *ethics* of the Darwinian revelation, though following from the same
premises, and almost as inevitably, are yet to be
generally realised. Darwin's revelation, like every
other revelation that has come to the world, is

perceived most tardily by those working in departments where the phenomena are the most intangible and complicated.

Darwin himself called 'the love for all living creatures the most noble attribute of man.' Giant as he was, he perceived more clearly than any of his contemporaries, more clearly even than his successors, the ultimate goal of evolving altruism. For he says: 'As man advances in civilisation, and small tribes are united into larger communities, the simplest reason would tell each individual that he ought to extend his social instincts and sympathies to all members of the same nation, though personally unknown to him. There is, then, only an artificial barrier to prevent his sympathies extending to the men of all nations and races. Experience, however, shows us how long it is, if such men are separated from him by great differences of appearance or habits, before he looks upon them as his fellow-creatures. Sympathy beyond the confines of man is one of the latest moral acquisitions. It is apparently unfelt by savages, except for their pets. The very idea of humanity, so far as I could observe, was new to most of the Gauchos of the Pampas. This virtue seems to arise from our sympathies becoming more tender and more widely diffused, until they are extended to all sentient beings' (7).

The influences of a doctrine old enough and precious enough to have become embodied in the life and institutions of a race persist generally, through mere momentum, long after the substance of the doctrine has passed away. This is eminently true of that misconception which has come down to us regarding the nature and origin of man and his relations to the rest of the universe. Darwin has lived, shed his light over the world, and passed back to the dust whence he came. Men no longer believe that other races and other worlds were really made for them. But they continue to *act* in about the same manner as they did when they *did* believe it. This assertion applies not simply to those half-baked intelligences who have only the rudest and most antiquated notions about anything but also to thousands of men and women who pretend to have up-to-date conceptions of themselves and the universe—men and women noted even for their activity in reminding others of their inconsistency—men and women who

> ' Compound for sins they are inclined to,
> By damning those they have no mind to.'

The doctrine of Universal Kinship is not a new doctrine, born from the more brilliant loins of modern understanding. It is as old almost as human philosophy. It was taught by Buddha twenty-four hundred years ago. And the teachings of this divine soul, spreading over the plains and peninsulas of Asia, have made unnumbered millions mild. It was taught also by Pythagoras and all his school of philosophers, and rigidly practised in their daily lives. Plutarch, one of the grandest characters of antiquity, wrote several essays in advocacy of it. In these essays, as well as in many passages of his writings generally, he demonstrates that he was far ahead of his contemporaries in the breadth and intensity of his moral nature, and in advance even of all except a very few of those living to-day, 2,000 years after him.   Shelley among the poets of modern times, and Tolstoy in these latter days, are others among the eminent adherents of this holy cause.

Wherever Buddhism prevails, there will be found in greater or less purity, as one of the cardinal principles of its founder, the doctrine of the sacredness of all Sentient Life.   But the Aryan race of the West has remained steadfastly deaf to the pleadings of its Shelleys and Tolstoys, owing to the overmastering influence of its anthropocentric religions.   Not till the coming of Darwin and his school of thinkers was there a basis for hope of a reformed world.   To-day the planet is *ripe* for the old-new doctrine.   Tradition is losing its power over men's conduct and conceptions as never before, and Science is growing more and more influential.   A central truth of the Darwinian philosophy is the unity and consanguinity of all organic life.   And during the next century or two the ethical corollary of this truth is going to receive unprecedented recognition in all departments of human thought.   Ignorance and Inertia are fearful facts.   They endure like granite in the human mind.   But the tireless chisels of evolution are invincible.   And the time will come when the anthropocentric customs and conceptions, which are to-day fashionable enough to be 'divine,' will have nothing but a historic existence. The movement to put Science and Humanitarianism in place of Tradition and Savagery, which is so weak, languishing, and neglected to-day, is a movement which has for its ultimate destiny the conquest of the Human Species.

XII. Conclusion.

All beings are *ends; no* creatures are *means.* All beings have not equal rights, neither have all men; but *all have rights.* The *Life Process* is the *End—not man,* nor any other animal temporarily privileged to weave a world's philosophy. Non-human beings were not made for human beings any more than human beings were made for non-human beings. Just as the sidereal spheres were once supposed by the childish mind of man to be unsubstantial satellites of the earth, but are known by man's riper understanding to be worlds with missions and materialities of their own, and of such magnitude and number as to render terrestrial insignificance frightful, so the billions that dwell in the seas, fields, and atmospheres of the earth were in like manner imagined by the illiterate children of the race to be the mere trinkets of men, but are now known by all who can interpret the new revelation to be beings with substantially the same origin, the same natures, structures, and occupations, and the same general rights to life and happiness, as we ourselves.

In their phenomena of life the inhabitants of

the earth display endless variety. They swim in the waters, soar in the skies, squeeze among the rocks, clamber among the trees, scamper over the plains, and glide among the grounds and grasses. Some are born for a summer, some for a century, and some flutter their little lives out in a day. They are black, white, blue, golden, all the colours of the spectrum. Some are wise and some are simple; some are large and some are microscopic; some live in castles and some in bluebells; some roam over continents and seas, and some doze their little day-dream away on a single dancing leaf. But they are all the children of a common mother and the co-tenants of a common world. Why they are here in this world rather than some place else; why the world in which they find themselves is so full of the undesirable; and whether it would not have been better if the ball on which they ride and riot had been in the beginning sterilised, are problems too deep and baffling for the most of them. But since they *are* here, and since they are too proud or too superstitious to die, and are surrounded by such cold and wolfish immensities, what would seem more proper than for them to be kind to each other, and helpful, and dwell together as loving and forbearing members of One Great Family?

ACT TOWARD OTHERS AS YOU WOULD ACT TOWARD A PART OF YOUR OWN SELF.

This is *The Great Law*, the all-inclusive gospel of social salvation. It is the rule of social rectitude and perfection which has been held up in greater or less perfection in all ages by the sages and prophets of the human species.

Hear Confucius, the giant of Mongolia, and the idol and law-giver of one-third of mankind :

' What you do not like when done to yourself do not do to others.'

And again he says :

' Do not let a man practise to those beneath him that which he dislikes in those above him.'

Over and over again the illustrious master repeats these precepts to his disciples and countrymen.

In the Mahabharata, the great epic of the Sanskrit, written by Indian moralists in various ages, and representing the accumulated wisdom of one of the most marvellous of all peoples, we find these words :

' Treat others as thou wouldst thyself be treated.'

' Do nothing to thy neighbour which thou wouldst not hereafter have thy neighbour do to thee.'

' A man obtains a rule of action by looking upon his neighbour as himself.'

These same truths were also taught by Jesus, that godlike Galilean, the great teacher and saviour of the Western world :

' Love thy neighbour as thyself.'

' Do unto others as you would have others do unto you.'

Oh that these words were etched in fire, and stamped in scorching characters on the dull, cold hearts of this world !

ACT TOWARD OTHERS AS YOU WOULD ACT
TOWARD A PART OF YOUR OWN SELF.

Look upon and treat others as you do your own
hands, your own eyes, your very heart and soul
—with infinite care and compassion—as suffering
and enjoying members of the same Great Being
with yourself. This is the spirit of the ideal
universe—the spirit of your own being. It is
this alone that can redeem this world, and give
to it the peace and harmony for which it longs.
Yes,

> ' So many gods, so many creeds,
> So many paths that wind and wind,
> While just the art of being kind
> Is all the sad world needs.'

Oh the madness, and sorrow, and unbrotherli-
ness of this mal-wrought world! Oh the poor,
weak, poisoned, monstrous natures of its children!
Who can look upon it all without pain, and
sympathy, and consternation, and tears? What
an opportunity for philanthropy, if the 'All-
mighty One' of our traditions would only set
about it !

Yes, do as you would be done by—and *not* to the
dark man and the white woman alone, but to the
sorrel horse and the gray squirrel as well; *not* to
creatures of your own anatomy only, but to *all*
creatures. You cannot go high enough nor low
enough nor far enough to find those whose bowed
and broken beings will not rise up at the coming
of the kindly heart, or whose souls will not shrink
and darken at the touch of inhumanity. Live and

let live. Do *more*. Live and *help* live. *Do to beings below you as you would be done by beings above you.* Pity the tortoise, the katydid, the wild-bird, and the ox. Poor, undeveloped, untaught creatures! Into their dim and lowly lives strays of sunshine little enough, though the fell hand of man be never against them. They are our fellow-mortals. They came out of the same mysterious womb of the past, are passing through the same dream, and are destined to the same melancholy end, as we ourselves. Let us be kind and merciful to them.

> ' Wilt thou draw near the nature of the gods ?
> Draw near them, then, in being merciful ;
> Sweet mercy is nobility's true badge.'

Let us be true to our ideals, true to the spirit of Universal Compassion—whether we walk with the lone worm wandering in the twilight of consciousness, the feathered forms of the fields and forests, the kine of the meadows, the simple savage on the banks of the gladed river, the political blanks whom men call wives, or the outcasts of human industry.

Oh this poor world, this poor, suffering, ignorant, fear-filled world ! How can men be blind or deranged enough to think it is a good world ? How can they be cold and satanic enough to be unmoved by the groans and anguish, the writhing and tears, that come up from its unparalleled afflictions ?

But *the world is growing better*. And in the

Future—in the long, long ages to come—IT WILL
BE REDEEMED! The same spirit of sympathy
and fraternity that broke the black man's manacles
and is to-day melting the white woman's chains
will to-morrow emancipate the working man and
the ox; and, as the ages bloom and the great
wheels of the centuries grind on, the same spirit
shall banish Selfishness from the earth, and
convert the planet finally into one unbroken and
unparalleled spectacle of PEACE, JUSTICE, and
SOLIDARITY.

BIBLIOGRAPHY

(1) SPENCER : Principles of Ethics, vol. i. ; New York,
1893.
(2) MAINE : Early History of Institutions ; New York, 1869.
(3) TENNENT : Natural History of Ceylon; London, 1861.
(4) MYERS : Ancient History, part i. ; Boston, 1899.
(5) MYERS : Ancient History, part ii. ; Boston, 1899.
(6) PRESTON AND DODGE : The Private Life of the Romans ;
Boston, 1896.
(7) DARWIN : Descent of Man ; London, 1874.
(8) HAMLEY : Our Poor Relations ; Boston, 1872.

VIII. VERTE-BRATES

5. MAMMALS
- 11. *Primates:* Man, monkey.
- 10. *Carnivora:* Dog, lion, skunk.
- 9. *Ungulates:* Ox, horse, deer.
- 8. *Sirenians:* Dugong.
- 7. *Cetaceans:* Whale, porpoise.
- 6. *Chiroptera:* Bat.
- 5. *Insectivora:* Mole, hedgehog.
- 4. *Rodents:* Rat, mouse, beaver.
- 3. *Edentates:* Sloth, ant-eater.
- 2. *Marsupials:* Kangaroo, opossum.
- 1. *Monotremes:* Duckbill, echidna.

4. BIRDS : Ostrich, owl, lark
3. REPTILES : Snake, lizard, turtle.
2. AMPHIBIANS : Frog, salamander.
1. FISHES : Shark, salmon, lung-fish.

VII. ARTHRO-PODS
- 4. ARACHNIDS : Spider, tick, king-crab.
- 3. INSECTS : Ant, fly, bug, beetle.
- 2. CRUSTACEANS : Crayfish, crab, barnacle.
- 1. MYRIAPODS : Centiped, milliped.

VI. MOLLUSKS : Clam, oyster, snail, squid.

V. WORMS : Earthworm, leech, trichina.

IV. ECHINODERMS : Star-fish, sea-urchin.

III. CELENTERATES : Hydra, coral, jelly-fish.

II. PORIFERA : Sponge.

I. PROTOZOA : Amœba, euglena, paramecium.

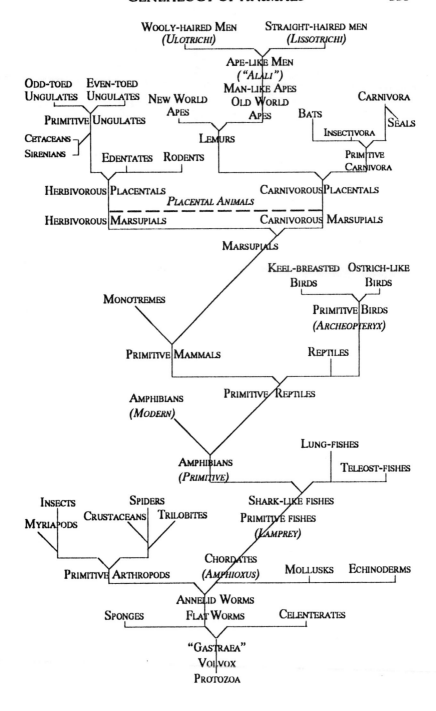

Appendix A
Four Letters from
J. Howard Moore to
Henry S. Salt

(There is some indication that these four letters, along with fifteen others, were sent to Jennie Darrow Moore, via a member of the Darrow family, by Henry S. Salt in 1921, five years after Moore's death.)

[1906]

Mr Dear Mr Salt,

I think of 53 Chancery Lane[1] as a sort of divine *abattoir* where the opponents of righteousness on this earth are scientifically

[1] The London address of The Humanitarian League. Ed.

slaughtered. I have just finished re-reading your incomparable little book on "The Logic of Vegetarianism." It is the best thing on this subject in existence — bold, brilliant, many-sided, unanswerable. I am glad you are on earth. *If it were not for a very few souls like you, this world would seem to me an intellectual solitude.* Fight on, my noble Brother. Your sword is from the armory of heaven. You'll never be paid nor properly appreciated for what you are doing. But you know I admire and love you. Your little book is capable of laying low kingdoms of carnivora. You are kind to send me a copy of the pretty new edition.

Always yours
J. Howard Moore
Chicago 4/20

My Dear Mr. Salt

I am going to write to you right now in answer to your nice letter just at hand; for I find when I put such things off I am likely to overdo the matter. But I shall have to use this perforated paper. I did not discover that my supply of letter paper was exhausted until after I had decided to write you.

Well, now I know what you mean when you tell me that circumstances have been driving you from your pretty cottage home. I am sorry indeed that you have had to suffer these changes. But if they eventuate in your going to live in the beautiful Lake Country, maybe it won't be so bad after all. You ought to live among the earth's highlands somewhere. One whose soul is so exalted as yours and so touched with poetry should live close to the sky.

O, yes, my brother, I should be much pleased to receive a copy of your book on James Thomson. I am always glad to read anything that flows from your unusual pen. "Sad and wonderful" — how attractive those words. I am always interested in any being or thing that is sad and wonderful.

I fear I cannot help you much in suggesting a publisher for your Life of Thoreau over here — if you think the regular publishers would not do. Charles H. Kerr & Co. of Chicago publish my B-W. Philosophy, and Universal Kinship. But they are a socialist publishing house, and print nothing except socialist and social science books. They do not publish my New Ethics, because it is not in their line. Don't you think firms like Macmillan might take up your Thoreau? Or some of the Boston houses? It seems anomalous that the best book ever written on this great American should not be printed in this country. I would do anything you might suggest in furthering an American edition of your work. Don't you suppose Dr. Emerson might be interested in the matter? He would probably be well acquainted with things at Boston.

I am not doing much in a literary way. Writing is so unnatural and hard for me that I have a good deal of difficulty in getting myself to undergo the hardship. It's a good deal like "sweating blood" for me. And unless I am driven by terrible feelings or convictions, I am inclined to go on and do nothing. I hate writing. It is the greatest hardship of my life. It seems to me I might be reasonably happy if I weren't everlastingly nagged by the obligation to perpetrate literary things on people. I have an idea, "The Evaluation of Mutualism", that I suppose I may finish in the next 3 or 4 years. It would be a discussion of the genesis and development of animal mutualism, especially human mutualism, with a forecast of some of the probabilities in this department of organic phenomena.

J. Howard Moore
Chicago, Oct 2, 1908

Citronelle, Alabama
3/25/1911

Mr Dear Mr. Salt,

I have not heard from you for a long time. And your silence has been contemporaneous with a rather dark time of my life. I have missed your kind and healing lines as the gloomy days crawled by.

I am down here in this little Alabama town 33 miles from Mobile, getting on my feet again after a slight break-down from overwork. I haven't been in school since the Christmas holidays. I am much better, and hope to be back in the Lake Country and at work soon.

In the last 16 or 17 years I have written 5 books. They may never amount to much, but I have given an immense amount of work to their production. I have taught all the time. And my literary work has all been done mornings and evenings, Saturdays and Sundays, and holidays and vacations. And it has been too much for my not naturally strong body.

This is a new world to me. It is the first time I have ever been in the Gulf Country. If I should ever have the pleasure of seeing and talking with you I would tell you about it.

Mr. Darrow (Clarence) and his brother Everett and families are going to Europe this summer. They expect to be in England, and I hope they may have the pleasure of seeing you. They are both of them excellent men - Everett being the more intellectual of the two. But they are essentially conservative and rather inconsistent in their attitude toward things. It will do them good to run up against a person so eminently consistent as yourself.

I love and admire you always, Mr. Salt.

J. Howard Moore

[1914]
Chicago, 12/4

My Dear Mr. Salt

The years go by, and you and I and all those
that breathe move on slowly and fatefully
toward the time when we shall give place to
others. In those years, now considerably
receded into the past, when the scales of
tradition first began to fall from my eyes, I
read a sentence from Tyndall that I never
have forgotten. It was the closing sentence of
an address before the British Association of
Science, and he was referring to a time in the
future when he and all his hearers would be
gone from the earth, and he said — "When
you and I, like fleecy clouds, shall have
melted into the infinite azure of the past". It
seems like such a poetic and euphemistic
way of referring to the tragedy of human
dissolution. This is my birthday. I am 52.
But I feel younger than I did 25 years ago.

No, I didn't go to Alabama this summer.
It's a little too hot down there in the summer
time. I was at home all summer — played
golf. I am going to my blessed acres in the
spring. Just this evening I sent a cheque for
the final payment. Now, (in a few days) I
shall have 116½ acres there of the loveliest
wild woods of pine, poplar, gum, beech, live
oak, magnolia, and holly. I have one holly
tree that is over a foot in diameter — and
magnolias like sawlogs. In my will I say "My
Alabama acres to be kept as they are forever
— as a sanctuary for the wild things and a

play place for men". People have told me over and over that I will never make anything out of the place. This reminder makes me tired. I wouldn't make anything out of it if I could. I bought it, not as an investment, but as an entertainment. It was Mr. E.E. Darrow who first called my place "Alligatoria". And we have so often referred to it playfully by that name that it seems to fit all right, and so I think I'll just christen it officially Alligatoria. There is no building on the place and it is away off from everywhere — and this last fact is what makes it so specially attractive to me. I can dream there all day and never see any one — except the red birds and squirrels, and great turtles dozing in the sun and the fishes and the great cranes circling above and hear the occasional grunt of an alligator. I got it cheap — and would gladly give you ten acres if you'd come over some time and go down there with me and fall in love with it. I have about a mile of water front — river and brook!

A word about the war. You didn't say how you are feeling about it, except to say that you are in mourning. It *is* a sad spectacle. But, as the French say, it had to be. The over-egoism and conceit of the Germans have brought it on. Germany has been preparing so definitely for the struggle. And so long as this one nation insisted upon it, it was inevitable. My sympathies are all with England and France. I never admired England so much in my life. You all there on that island seem almost like brothers and sisters. Clarence Darrow and wife were over the other evening, and Mr.

Darrow says he was never so much interested in anything else in his life. He thinks, as I do, that America should go to the assistance of the Allies rather than *see* Germany dominant. The war has served to build up a strong feeling of affinity between Americans and other English-speaking peoples. I am hoping that this tragedy will render people so sick of war that we shall make a long, big stride toward permanent and formal peace when it is over. But Germany *must be put down*. The earth would not be a fit place for non-Germans to live if the Germans were victorious. So there is only one thinkable outcome of it all in a military way — the utter annihilation of the menace of Prussianism. The Germans are not barbarians by any means, but they are showing many unmistakably barbarous traits.

J. Howard Moore

Appendix B
Address Delivered
at the Funeral Service of
John Howard Moore
by
Clarence S. Darrow

John Howard Moore was my brother and my friend. He lies here dead while we still live and move around him. His was a noble soul, else he would not be in his casket now. He loved men and animals, the birds, the bees and all living things. His clay was so sensitive and fine that he rejoiced when they rejoiced and suffered in their pain. His brain was strong, but his vital organs were weak. His life was filled with deeds of kindness for all living things and his mind was devoted to lessening the suffering of the world. In every book he wrote and almost every word he spoke he urged the blind and heartless world to be merciful and kind. He wrote of the kinship of all living things and he believed in every word he wrote and spoke. He was a teacher, who cared not what the world had taught, but with all patience and labor sought to learn and teach the truth, not alone the literal things which most men call truth, but facts illumined and softened, and humanized by the touch of kinship, sympathy, and an abiding love. We who knew him best will miss him most, but the dumb beasts for whom he spoke and the helpless songsters that he loved, all unconsciously will miss his noble words which ever plead for justice and for kindness to these helpless ones.

For many patient hours, through long years, he had listened to the birds, until from their cries and songs he had learned to understand the language that they used — to tell the feelings of their pent up souls.

Few men who ever lived were so thoughtful of all other life and so devoted to the noble task of enlightening human minds and softening human deeds. Little wonder that in his last pathetic note his words were for the "four footed" that he loved.[1] His was a tender

---

[1] "The long struggle is ended. I must pass away. Good-bye. Oh, men are so cold and hard and half conscious toward their suffering fellows. Nobody understands. O my mother! and O, my little girl! What will become of you? And the poor four footed? May the long years be merciful.

"Take me to my river. There, where the wild birds sing and the waters go on and on, alone in my groves, forever.

"O, Tess, forgive me. O, forgive me please."

heart, a noble brain and a nature so sensitive and fine that in his imagination he lived the lives of every thing that breathes, and men like him cannot die old. When poor clay is so mixed as to make a man like John Howard Moore, even an unfeeling universe must rejoice, but bitter is the cup that he must drink and hopeless the sorrow he must feel.

John Howard Moore was a fool, one of those rare devoted fools, who thought that his words and life could help a world that will not listen and cannot see, and therefore does not feel.

I loved the dead too well to neglect to say what he would have me say, that he put a pistol to his brain and ended his own life. At least he took his life as much as any human being does any act, but no one can make a choice and every thought and deed is compelled by forces infinitely stronger than any human life.

He went out in the morning into Jackson Park, on the wooded island, the place he loved, where for years he had listened to his friends, the song birds, lay down upon the grass, put a pistol to his head and sent a bullet through his brain. He lived a noble life and died a heroic death. I honor and love him for the life he lived, and give him my unbounded admiration for the death he died.

Of all the millions born into this world, none have any choice of coming and almost none make any choice of going. He was one of those who chose his time and place to die; one of the few rare men who were "Masters of their fate, and captains of their souls."

The coroner's jury passing on his death determined that "he died from his own hand while suffering under a temporary fit of insanity." In fact "he died from his own hand while suffering under a temporary fit of sanity." No man can open his eyes upon the truth and live; and that human life may be preserved "we see as through a glass darkly," and all the facts of the universe are softened, bent and twisted so we may not realize that life is life and death is death.

Man does not live by truth, but by the illusions that his brain conceives. Life is short and hard and so he fashions heaven given to everlasting peace and joy. The present he knows is disappointing, but the future will be good. Pain and sorrow he feels to-day, but happiness will come to-morow.

Nature has planted deep in all sentient things the "will to live", and that the earth may ever bring forth the sons of men, she lures them with a thousand vain imaginings until with a mocking laugh she lands them in the open grave.

John Howard Moore had no dream of heaven, no hope of life beyond the tomb; but he saw the injustice and misery of the world and found inspiration and activity in vain efforts to make the earth a better and a kindlier place. He lived and wrote and worked with feverish haste and believed that the blind and heartless world would listen to his words and mend its ways.[1] But humanity

[1] His chief works were The Universal Kinship, Better World Philosophy, The New Ethics and The Law of Biogenesis.

went on trading and dickering, lying and cheating, marrying and dying, and never heard his voice. One day he opened his eyes and knew his work was vain, and feeling the weight of the universal sorrow on his soul, he took his life. Do not ask why he killed himself, but rather why one so sensitive and wise and brave and kind could have lived so long.

This man, our brother, never purposely killed a living thing until he put the pistol to his head.

Poor dead dreamer, you are not the first or last mortal to learn the truth. Other men like you have flung their quivering hearts to the thankless wolves and felt them tearing the flesh to bits; others have wakened from the mad and blissful dream of saving mankind from itself. When the cruel wakening comes, some turn their hearts to stone and play the game, some live in blind despair; our brother put a bullet in his brain.

This brave and loving man had richly earned the right to die; he left no debt unpaid; no duty undone; no obligation unfulfilled; and no one human or divine has the right to condemn his act.

I have dreamed my dreams, had my illusions and wakened from my sleep. Why do I not follow him? I do not end it all because the love of life and the shrinking fear of death in all living things stays my hand and my courage fails.

For the loved ones he left behind and the friends who knew his voice, I can find no honest words of consolation and of hope.

"Not all the preaching since Adam
Can make death other than death."

In the presence of the relentless harvester,
all sham and pretence should be cast aside.
One ought to speak the truth, with no thought
to delude others or ourselves.

Now hollow fires burn out to black,
And lights are guttering low:
Square your shoulders, lift your pack,
And leave your friends and go.

Oh never fear, man, nought's to dread,
Look not left nor right:
In all the endless road you tread
There's nothing but the night.

Amongst all who are gathered here, there
is but one whom we can felicitate on this
event, and that one is our friend who lies
peaceful and all unconscious of the world. If
any word of mine could call back his troubled
soul, I should feel myself guiltier far if I
brought him back than I would to cause a
brother's death.

The dead left his request that his ashes
should be taken to his wild wood home in
Alabama and laid beside the river in the
forest where he could sleep in peace forever.

Well, dear friend, you shall be taken to the
spot you wished — far from the haunts of
men and laid in the earth where come the
birds and beasts you loved. There, at least,
you will be at rest, and feel no more the cruel
sufferings of the world. There the river will

murmur on forever as it runs past your tomb, but no sound can reach your ears. The wild birds will sing their everlasting songs of love and hope about your grave, all unconscious of their friend who slumbers there, and who can never more be gladdened by their joy or suffer with their pain.

*This address was published in **The Athena**, Park Ridge, Illinois, October 1916, pp. 21-3.*

Appendix C
Publications by J. Howard Moore

1. *Why I Am a Vegetarian.* An address delivered before the Chicago Vegetarian Society, Great Northern Hotel, March 3, 1895, Chicago. Chicago: Ward Waugh, 1895. 42pp.
2. "Why I Am a Vegetarian," *Chicago Vegetarian*, September 1897, 5-9; October 1897, 5-9; November 1897, 8-12; December 1897, 7-11, 16, 18.
3. "Clerical Sportsmen," *Chicago Vegetarian*, November 1898, 5-6.
4. *Better-World Philosophy: A Sociological Synthesis.* Chicago: Ward Waugh, 1899, 275pp. Second edition, London: Bell, 1907, 275pp. Also Chicago: C.H. Kerr, 1906, 275pp. Chapter titles: The Problem of Industry, Blunders, The Social Problem, Egoism and Altruism, The Preponderance of Egoism, The Social Ideal, Origin of Human Nature, Race Culture, Individual Culture. "$1.10 postpaid"
5. *America's Apostasy.* Chicago: Ward Waugh, 1899, 4pp. (Concerning the Philippine islands.)

6. "How Vegetarians Observe the Golden Rule," *The Vegetarian and Our Fellow Creatures*, August 15, 1901, 295-7.
7. *The Universal Kinship.* Chicago: C.H. Kerr, 1906, 329 pp. Also 1908 and 1916 editions published by C.H. Kerr. Also London: Bell and Sons, 1906. Also London: Humanitarian League, 1906.
8. *The New Ethics.* London: E. Bell, 1907, 216 pp. Revised edition, Chicago: S.A. Block, 1909. Chapter titles: The Nature of Opinion, The Thesis of the New Ethics, The Human Attitude Towards Others, Silent Martyrs of Civilization, The Cost of a Skin, What Shall We Eat?, Is Man a Plant-eater?, The Food of the Future, The Peril of Over-population, The Survival of the Strenuous, Flashlights on Human Progress, Conclusion. "$1.10 Postpaid"
9. "Silent Martyrs of Civilization," 1908, non-paginated.
10. "Humane Teaching in Schools," 8 pp., an essay bound with several other essays, most of them originally printed by the Humantarian League, under the general title *The Treatment of Animals* (publisher and date not indicated; probably about 1910).
11. *Fermented Beverages: Their Effects on Mankind.* Revised edition, 64 pp. London: Harrison and Sons, 1910?
12. *Ethics and Education.* London: G. Bell and Sons, 1912, 188 pp.
13. *The Ethics of School Life.* London: G. Bell, 1912, 24 pp.
14. *High School Ethics.* London: G. Bell, 1912. "Lessons given in the Crane Technical High School in my work as an instructor in the Department of Ethics."
15. "Discovering Darwin," proceedings of the International Anti-Vivisection and Animal Protection Congress, Hotel Raleigh, Washington D.C., December 8-11, 1913, pp. 152-8.

16. *The Law of Biogenesis: Two Lessons on the Origin of Human Nature*. Chicago: C.H. Kerr, 1914, 123 pp. "The material in this book was given originally as lectures in the Crane Technical High School, Chicago." Also Slovenian edition, Chicago: Slovenska Narodna Podporna Jednota, 1920.

17. *Savage Survivals*. Chicago: C.H. Kerr, 1916, 191 pp. Also 1934 edition by C.H. Kerr. "The material in this book was given originally as lectures in the Crane Technical High School, Chicago. The lectures formed a part of a larger course of lectures on the subject of ethics." Also London: Watts and Co., 1918 and 1919 and 1927 and 1933. Also Solvenian edition, Chicago: Novi Svijet, 1924.

18. "Evidences of Relationship," *Our Dumb Animals*, Massachusetts Society for the Prevention of Cruelty to Animals, Volume 47, No. 3, August, 1914. "Man-like Apes", pp. 33-4; "Monkeys", pp. 51-2; "Dogs", pp. 69-70; "Ants", p. 87.

19. "The Contemporary Lessons of Galileo," reprinted from *The Conservator*, date unknown, one page.

INDEX

(Prepared by Charles Magel, 1992)

353